3⁵⁰

THE THUNDER MAKER

THE
THUNDER MAKER

General Thomas Meagher

WILLIAM M. LAMERS

Illustrated by VERA YTTRI

THE BRUCE PUBLISHING COMPANY
MILWAUKEE

Library of Congress Catalog Card Number: 59–10973

CONTENTS

Chapter I

ROUGH WEATHER ON AN
ENGLISH HEATH

CHRISTMAS season was coming close in the year
1841, and the young men of Stonyhurst College, a
famous English Jesuit school, had been preparing for
months to produce Shakespeare's *King Lear*.

Every year at Christmas time the Stonyhurst students produced three plays, a farce, a comedy, and
a tragedy. "Without our plays," the students agreed,
"it wouldn't seem like Christmas to us. Why, if they
wouldn't let us have our plays, we'd have a riot."
Christmas plays were an important tradition at Stony-

1

hurst. If they were stopped, so the students thought, all the discipline in the school would break down.

This year they were saying, "Just wait until you hear Meagher as Kent."

Tom Meagher, handsome, slender, blue-eyed, was seventeen years old. Everybody knew Tom Meagher, although he had been at Stonyhurst only four months. He was the best talker in the school. He loved fun. He had a kind disposition, but a fighting heart.

The college prided itself on its large theater, although, judged by modern standards, it could not have been altogether comfortable. The spectators sat on benches arranged in semicircles, each row back a little higher until the last was thirty feet above the first. Behind a brilliantly gilded arch, the stage extended back forty feet from the footlights. The large stage was well equipped too. The students, especially those from rural areas, admired its brilliantly painted scenery.

Best of all was the equipment for making storms. From one of the frames holding a rolled-up scene — a "drop" — a large sheet of iron was hung. When this was shaken it gave a rattle and rumble like the best thunder. Next to this thunder sheet stood a long box, partly filled with shot, which made a sighing sound like rain when tipped and shaken. To imitate lightning, an arrangement was set up to blow powdered resin into a candle flame, where it burned with a flash.

The Stonyhurst Dramatic Society was proud of this equipment. When King Lear strode upon the heath in a storm, they would give him plenty of bad weather as background for his misery and complaints.

Everyone expected a violent storm. But they got a bigger storm than they expected when Father William Johnson appointed Meagher the thunder maker.

Meagher was to become a specialist in making storms. He was to make thunder on three continents. And the thunder he made on the stage at Stonyhurst was worthy of him.

It almost broke up the play.

For fifty generations through fifteen centuries a chief of the tribe of O'Meagher — sometimes spelled Maher — ruled the ancestral land of O'Carin's territory in Tipperary County, Ireland.

The Meaghers had a fiery, unconquerable spirit which they kept even in the black days of Ireland's gloom. Like many another Irish family, they lost what was left of a once considerable inheritance of lands, castles, and other wealth in the wars which the Irish fought against Oliver Cromwell and the kings of England who followed after him. But the Meaghers never lost their fighting spirit or their good heads.

In the late 1700's, many Irishmen left their unhappy island to seek new homes elsewhere. Some of these went to Newfoundland. Among this group was a man by the name of Meagher who had been a farmer in Tipperary.

Meagher prospered in the New World. His family grew up around him in comfortable circumstances. One day he called his son, Thomas, to speak to him.

"Thomas," he said, "things have gone mighty well with us here, thanks be to God. When I look back on how I began, and remember my climb from trader to merchant, and merchant to ship owner, I am astonished."

"You have done very well, Father."

"And for the sake of all of you, I would like to do better. Now, Thomas, I want you to return to Ireland as my representative and take charge of things there." The Meagher ships carried on a prosperous business with Ireland.

Thus it happened that Thomas Meagher left Newfoundland to take up residence in Ireland, at Waterford, a beautiful port on the southwest coast. There he became a prominent, prosperous citizen and married a young lady named Quan. There their first child was born on August 23, 1823. The boy was baptized Thomas Francis Meagher.

Young Tom Meagher spent the first ten years of his life in Waterford. He was an unusually bright boy and attended the best school in the city. He enjoyed walking through the town and hearing about the famous people who had lived there and the historic events that had taken place. He learned much Irish history from the talk at his father's table, from conversation with people in the streets, from living in a city where some of it had been made.

Less than a mile from his home, but across the bridge of the Suir River which runs through Waterford, is a high hill called Mount Misery. Climbing to the summit Tom Meagher could look down on the city with its houses and church steeples, the river, the sparkling bay, and the beautiful green countryside. In the distance he could see the hunched foothills and, beyond them, the Commeragh Mountains.

Tom Meagher loved to climb Mount Misery, to sit watching the day turn into evening, and evening into night. He grew to love Ireland, its people, its history, its scenery. When he was still a boy, his mother died and was buried in Irish soil. Now Tom had another great reason for loving Ireland.

By the time he was ten years old, Tom was a sturdy-legged, warmhearted boy, popular in school and with the neighbors, and much loved in his happy family. His mother's sister joined the household to take care of Tom and his brother Henry. It was at this time while walking along the Waterford docks — the "quay" it was called — Tom saw a scene that changed his life.

A ship lay at anchor along the quay, waiting the tide to leave the harbor. On its deck huddled hundreds of men, women, and children. Their thin faces showed the famine they had suffered. Their small bundles of possessions and shabby clothes revealed their poverty. They were strangely and terribly quiet, so that even a carefree boy of ten understood their grief at leaving a land and people they loved.

Tom turned to his father. "Where are they going?" he asked.

"To America."

"But why are they leaving Ireland?"

Mr. Meagher looked grim. "Well, it's a long, sad story, Tom, and I can't tell it all to you now. But you'll learn — you'll learn —"

For centuries the English conquerors had treated the Irish badly, sometimes cruelly. The story of this persecution is one of the longest and most unpleasant in history. Millions of Irish through the difficult years left the island, seeking happier homes elsewhere.

It would be harder to understand such persecution if we could not pick up our newspaper and read about similar persecutions today. The Irish were not the only people to be treated unjustly. Emigrant ships were waiting at docks at every seaport of Europe to carry the poor, the persecuted, the adventurous away from the poverty, persecution, and lack of opportunity of the Old World to better chances in the New. Hundreds of thousands of Englishmen were fleeing England.

But let there be no mistake: Ireland's misery was worse. The wrongs were greater and had lasted for centuries. The oppression was grimmer, the poverty more grinding and universal, the chances of living a full life much less.

As ten-year-old Tom Meagher looked at the huddled refugees, it seemed to him that Waterford suddenly changed. He had thought it a cheerful place. Now it took on an air of shabbiness and gloom. Moments ago the bells of Waterford peeled merrily for him. Now they tolled as for a funeral, sadly.

Tom Meagher had heard many stories about Ireland's misery. He had listened to them as a child listens to fairytales. Now he knew that they were real. Misrule in Ireland was real. Real people had suffered real hurts, and were still suffering. He never could shake the scene on the quay from his mind. That evening he became a lover of freedom, a lifelong hater of injustice, a warrior in the fight for liberty, an Irish patriot.

When he was eleven years old, Tom Meagher said good-by to his father, his aunt, and his brother Henry, and left Waterford to become a student at the Jesuit College at Clongowes-Wood, on the plain of County Kildare, in east-middle Ireland.

The college was housed in an old castle, a massive square of masonry, set off with great towers, standing on a hill in the midst of beautiful woods, and in the center of a circle of ancient, historic Irish towns. Here a grim chapter in Irish history had been written by Oliver Cromwell. Cromwell's soldiers had taken the castle's defenders to Dublin and there hanged them, after promising quarter, and then murdered the women and children. So great was the slaughter of the Irish by the Puritan army that summer, that not enough of them were left in fall to gather a twentieth part of the harvest they had planted in spring.

At Clongowes Tom Meagher not only learned more of the sad history of his native land but found an opportunity to develop a talent that would enable him to speak out in her defense.

"Tom, I'll look for you at the next meeting of the Debating Society."

"Debating Society? Sure, Father, I talk too much as it is. And as for arguing, no Irishman has to join a society to find something to argue about, or someone to argue with."

In the Debating Society Tom Meagher discovered that he had a great gift.

"Listen to that boy," one Jesuit would say to another. "He has the gift of tongues. Did you ever hear the likes of him?"

"He's the best talker in the college."

"He'll be the best talker in Ireland someday. He'll be as good as Daniel O'Connell — the Lord prosper the great man!"

"He'll be better than O'Connell."

"And have you read Tom's English compositions?"

"Marvelous, Father, marvelous."

"And best of all, he's a fine boy."

At Clongowes-Wood Tom was kind, generous, friendly. He liked to have good fun and he took part in the students' pranks. But he was exceptionally bright, and his brilliance in speaking and writing carried over into all his schoolwork so that he understood easily the difficult subjects that other students labored hard and long to understand.

In the college library Tom found an old book. "I loved it all the more because it was in rags," he said. In its company he spent the pleasantest hours at Clongowes. The book contained the principal speeches which two of the greatest Irish orators, O'Connell and Shiel, had made from 1825 to 1829. As Tom Meagher studied these speeches, he made up his mind to become a great orator like Shiel and O'Connell, and to speak out against the wrongs being done to Ireland and the Irish.

Tom Meagher received excellent training from the Jesuits at Clongowes-Wood. As a grown man he looked back and could find only one thing to criticize. The good Fathers knew too little about Irish history.

"They never spoke of Ireland. Never gave us her history to read," he complained. "They never told us about the martyrdoms, the wrongs, the statesmanship, the magnificent memories, and illuminating hopes of the dear old land."

Instead they talked about Grecian gods and goddesses, the history of ancient peoples and of England. They made reference to America. But surrounded by Irish history, in the midst of old battlefields, landmarks, graveyards, ruins, they knew little about these matters, and cared and said less.

Clongowes College was like a modern junior-senior high school. After six years of study there, Tom Meagher graduated. To complete his education, his father sent him to Stonyhurst College in England.

Stonyhurst was and is a famous English Jesuit school. Tom Meagher remembered the college as two towers topped with eagles, standing out of a deep valley, surrounded by high, barren hills. The valley had brooks running through it and was covered with thick stands of old trees. Beneath the fallen leaves and branches, pheasants, deer, and woodcock could be hunted.

During his four years at Stonyhurst, Thomas Meagher again proved to be a brilliant student. The professors of a school that had graduated many fine orators predicted that he would be one of the greatest among them. In English composition Meagher received the first prize. The hardest job he attempted at Stonyhurst was to lose some of his rich Irish brogue. The storm in *King Lear* was a part of the process. The storm took place at Christmas during Tom's first year at the English college.

Tom described his principal teacher during this year, Father William Johnson, S.J., as "very gentle, very kind, with the softest whisper for a voice." Father Johnson was ungainly, and although the boys laughed at his clumsiness, they loved him and admired him so much that had the faintest danger threatened him, "they'd have flung themselves before him and died for him." Father Johnson "thought that an Irish brogue was vulgar," and on hearing a boy say "bekase" instead of "because" he would hold his tattered handkerchief to his mouth.

"Meagher," he said again and again, coughing into his handkerchief, "that's a horrible brogue you have got."

When Father Johnson was assigned the task of directing the school production of *King Lear,* he thought he should give the brilliant Meagher boy a chance to act and assigned him the part of the Earl of Kent.

A week before Christmas, on the night of the first full dress rehearsal, Meagher barely had recited the lines

"Fare thee well, King; since thus thou wilt appear,
    Freedom lives hence, and banishment is near"
before Father Johnson cuffed him over the head with a large manuscript copy of the play.

"It will never do, Meagher," he said in disgust. "That frightful brogue of yours will never do for Shakespeare."

Knowing Father Johnson's dislike of the Irish brogue, all the characters, including old King Lear himself, began to chuckle and laugh while Meagher kept on reciting:

"Thus Kent, O princes, bids you all adieu;

He'll shape his old course to a bowing country new."

There was a sofa on the stage, and Meagher lay down on it. Father Johnson's face grew very red.

"Meagher, that brogue will never do. I must degrade you from the peerage. You'll have to be a common soldier. You'll carry a brown bill in the battle scenes. You'll make the thunder and rain in the tempest and turn the wind."

And so Tom Meagher exchanged costumes with another young man by the name of Clifford. Clifford was given the costume of an earl: a scarlet velvet hat with a plume in it, a silk cloak, a rich jacket, long silk hose, sandals, and a sword. Meagher got the uniform of a common soldier: a tin helmet, leather breastplate, a pair of shapeless leather shoes, and a battle-ax and spear.

Although both Meagher and Clifford received the same number of sandwiches that evening, Meagher felt that his loss of the part was unfair punishment for being Irish. But he had his revenge.

On the opening night he fastened Clifford's legs so tightly in the stocks that the servants had to carry both Clifford and the stocks off the stage to get him loose. In the battle of Dover Cliffs, Meagher swung his battle-ax so vigorously that he cut an imitation rock in two and knocked down half the cast.

But his big moment came when he made the storm. King Lear took the center of the stage to shout:

"Blow winds, and crack your cheeks! rage! blow!
You cataracts and hurricanes spout!"

And while he shouted, "with the frenzy of a fiend" Meagher rattled the thunder sheet, shook the rain box, and turned the crank of the wind machine. He blew the powdered resin into the candle flame and made "terrific" lightning.

Frantically Father Johnson tried to calm the storm. "Silence!" he commanded.

But the thunder grew louder, the rain more violent, the wind fiercer, and the lightning more brilliant.

"When I get off the stage, I'll kick you," Lear shouted, but no one but Meagher could hear him.

The Royal Physician threw a camp stool at Meagher, and Father Johnson shouted above the screaming wind, "You'll be flogged for this, Meagher. I'll make Rome howl."

Later, in the fourth act, when Tom entered the stage as a messenger, he wore the fool's cap instead of his tin helmet and carried a sandwich in the same hand as the battle-ax. Saluting King Lear's daughter, Cordelia, he announced in the richest brogue he could use that the "British peers are marching hitherward."

Knowing the Irish boy, his love of his country, and the story of how his brogue had cost him an important part in the play, the audience applauded and called on him to repeat the message. Then they burst into a great salvo of cheers for him.

In the years that followed, the world did not always cheer for the storms that Thomas Meagher made. But they never ceased to admire his courage.

Chapter II

SQUALLS OVER IRELAND

IN THE early summer of 1843, Thomas Meagher, a young man nearing twenty, returned home from Stonyhurst. His father was now mayor of Waterford, the first Catholic in Ireland to be elected to that high office in two hundred years. During that time the laws imposed by the English had not permitted Catholics to be so elected.

Had it not been for his religion, Meagher undoubtedly would have taken further studies at some English or Irish university.

"I could well afford to send you there, Tom," said

Mayor Meagher, "and it's a fine education you would get. But they aren't friendly to our Faith, and you might be losing it. And education in the law, or any other field, bought at that price is a poor bargain."

"I agree with you, Father," Tom answered.

"You could learn the law in other ways. Perhaps you could go to Dublin and study with a good lawyer. First, though, I think you ought to see a little more of Europe than Ireland and England. Maybe when you return you will know for certain what you want to do."

And so Mayor Meagher sent his older son to travel on the continent of Europe. Tom visited Germany, Holland, and Belgium before he returned home to celebrate his twentieth birthday.

These were exciting days in Ireland. Revolution was in the air, and for the first time in almost half a century the oppressed Irish were in a mood to strike a blow for their freedom.

For a brief period, up to 1798, Ireland had had its own parliament to make most of its laws, even though Catholics were excluded from holding seats in it. In most places in Ireland the population was almost entirely Catholic. In that year the English government, by its injustices, had goaded Irish Catholics and many Irish Protestants — some of the most important leaders were Protestant — into revolt. Having put down the revolution, the English parliament approved the Act of Union, which joined England and Ireland and placed the whole authority to rule Ireland in the English parliament.

Of course patriotic Irishmen protested against this further invasion of their rights, as they had protested against the wrongs committed by the English invaders who had first come to Ireland in 1169 and found it to their advantage to remain.

For more than 600 years the Irish were deprived of their rights. Again and again the country was invaded and ravaged.

When England ceased to be Catholic, the religious difference only made other differences harder to settle. The Catholic Irish were forbidden to practice their religion and taxed heavily to support a church to which they did not belong. Priests were hunted as outlaws. English garrisons were set upon the Irish. The Irish were forbidden to carry on certain kinds of trade and manufacture. They were denied the right to teach and to send their children to school. They could not hold most public offices. The best lands were taken from them. In short, they were treated a hundred times worse than the thirteen American colonies were treated.

The American colonies revolted against England once and gained their independence. The Irish revolted again and again, and up to Meagher's time had failed.

While it is not pleasant to think or write about such matters, they nevertheless are true, and history. At the same time we must remember that in England itself for these hundreds of years many Englishmen did not have the rights, privileges, and opportunities that decent, sensible people today feel everyone should have. There were many good people, too, in England who were in no way responsible for the bad treatment of Ireland and the Irish. And in our own times there are still bad governments which deny other persons, peoples, and nations their rights and rob, persecute, enslave, and even kill them.

Finally in 1823 Daniel O'Connell, the great Irish statesman and orator, founded the Catholic Association.

"Unarmed, we Catholics can't stand up to the power of the armies and navies of England. England is the strongest nation in the world; the British Empire, the greatest. But if all Irishmen, particularly the Catholics because they are in the great majority, will band together and present a peaceful yet firm common front to the English, the English will be forced, whether they will it or no, to give Ireland some measure of justice and freedom." This was O'Connell's thought, though not his precise language.

The history of the Catholic Association is too long and complicated to be told here. It is enough for us to know that by 1829 the laws of England had been so changed as to give Catholics the right to vote for members of the English parliament. Even more, Catholics could sit in that body, and Daniel O'Connell had been elected to the English House of Commons and, in 1830, had taken his seat.

Because O'Connell aimed not only to secure for Catholics the same rights of citizenship which Protestants enjoyed, but to repeal the hated Act of Union as well, he founded in 1840 the Loyal National Repeal Association. To enlist the support of people all over Ireland, the Association held "monster meetings." The largest of these took place in August, 1843, at Tara Hill, the seat of the ancient kings of Ireland.

When O'Connell stood on the speaker's platform on the top of the hill, he could look down on all sides on a stirring sea of humanity that stretched back until the human voice could not reach the outermost circle of it and the faces blurred with the distance.

"A million people!" was the fair estimate of the crowd that day.

"Sure and did you see the roads? The tens of thousands of carriages and carts."

"And the marching bands, hundreds and hundreds of them."

"And the temporary altars at the roadside. Faith, every Catholic here must have gone to Mass."

"And did you hear the sermon on temperance, too? I'd wager my soul that there's not a drunken person in the crowd."

"Nor a fight, either. Well, O'Connell told us to be sober and keep the peace."

"Look at the bishops and priests with him, and the blessed Father Matthew. God bless the Apostle of Irish Temperance!"

"Hush, the great man is beginning to speak."

"I can't hear him, but I can tell what O'Connell is saying by his gestures."

On September 24, 1843, on the evening before an immense meeting at Lismore, a large dinner was held at which O'Connell himself was present. At this event Tom Meagher made his first political speech. So well did he talk, that O'Connell, then perhaps the greatest orator in the world, clapped Tom on the back, and said, "Well done, Young Ireland."

Terrified by these great crowds, the English government tried to break O'Connell's power and forbade further meetings. It hoped that rioting would take place so that the English soldiers could interfere. But so great was the popularity of O'Connell that he was now called the "uncrowned King of Ireland," and he kept his followers from lawless acts. This restraint did not prevent the English from arresting him as a conspirator plotting to overthrow the government. The charge was trumped up, the trial unfair, and the verdict unjust. An English jury found O'Connell guilty and sentenced him to a fine and a year's imprisonment. Although O'Connell was released after three months, illness and old age, and the death of his hope that in six months he would set Ireland free shook his self-confidence. He came out of prison an old, broken man.

For two years after his speech at Lismore, Meagher made no more political speeches. Instead, he lived in Dublin and studied privately to be a lawyer.

"Do you like Dublin, Mr. Meagher?" he was asked.

"I do not like it. Many of the prominent people here try to act like Englishmen. They should be proud of being Irish and act like Irishmen."

When O'Connell and his friends were tried at the Queen's bench in Dublin, Meagher sometimes visited the law court. Sometimes he attended patriotic meetings. He made many friends among the best people in Ireland.

In September, 1845, the potato blight appeared in Ireland for the first time. The potato was the most common food of the poor Irish. When famine followed the crop failure, and pestilence followed famine, it seemed that nothing could add to the woes of Ireland.

It is the unpleasant truth that the English government appeared indifferent and debated while the helpless Irish died by the tens of thousands. And when America and other countries sent food, it did not always reach the starving Irish.

O'Connell's Repeal Movement had attracted a number of Irishmen fresh out of college. These enthusiastic young men soon grew impatient with O'Connell, and withdrawing from his leadership, established an independent organization which they called "Young Ireland." They borrowed this title from O'Connell's compliment to Meagher. To assist them in telling the Irish people how to right the wrong being done to them, they established a paper called the *Nation*.

Although the older men had been able to keep Meagher and his young friends from seizing control of the Repeal Association, they could not keep them from gaining many followers throughout Ireland. Three thousand of these gathered in October, 1846, in the Great Hall of the Rotunda in Dublin to listen to speakers. The most eloquent of these was Meagher.

"That meeting of Young Ireland made a powerful impression on the country," Daniel O'Connell was told. "The leaders are able, and Meagher is a fine spokesman."

"We must have them back," O'Connell answered. "I have written a letter to Meagher asking him to return to the Repeal Association."

Meagher declined to return. He told O'Connell that he did not believe in the methods used by the Association.

The Repealers still hoped to gain Ireland's liberties gradually, by working peaceably with the English. The Young Irelanders were willing, if necessary, to take up arms to fight for Ireland's freedom. But the break between the two groups was neither clear nor final for several years. Meanwhile, to carry out their purposes, Meagher and his friends founded the Irish Confederation in January, 1847.

With famine and pestilence raging in Ireland, and the Irish starving by the tens of thousands or flocking to the seaports to try to escape, the young men of the Association had a difficult job in gaining recruits. Nevertheless, before the year 1847 was over, they had established Confederation Clubs throughout the island and had enrolled more than ten thousand members. Although the Association attempted first of all to help the famine sufferers, it had little success in this effort.

At the same time the Confederation resolved to enter politics, and when Daniel O'Connell, Jr., son of the great orator, resigned as a member of parliament for Meagher's native city of Waterford, Meagher entered the race for the office. His father, who already was serving Waterford as a member of the English parliament, contributed money to his son's campaign. Nevertheless, in a close election, watched by all Ireland, Meagher lost.

Scarcely had this news been published when a more important story appeared in the headlines of the newspapers of the world. A revolution in France had pushed King Louis Phillippe from the throne. This successful revolution roused hope in the hearts of oppressed people everywhere.

So many revolutions took place in 1848 that history has called it "The Revolutionary Year." Some kind of upheaval took place in all the civilized governments of the world except those of the United States, Switzerland, and England. And England faced trouble in Ireland.

On February 12, 1848, twelve days before the successful French revolution, a new newspaper made its appearance in Ireland. This was the *United Irishmen*, edited by John Mitchel, a former writer for the *Nation*. The motto of Mitchel's paper was, "Our independence must be won at all hazards." Even some members of the Irish Confederation said that Mitchel talked like a madman. He openly preached armed revolution and told the readers of his paper how to carry it out.

In July, 1848, a meeting of the Repeal Association was held in Dublin. Meagher was selected as one of the speakers. By now he had made many speeches and was considered one of the ablest of the young Irish orators. The chairman of the meeting was John O'Connell, another son of Daniel O'Connell. The audience, cool to Meagher when he began, gradually warmed up to him, even though he spoke the language of Mitchel rather than O'Connell.

"The soldier is proof against an argument — but he is not proof against a bullet. The man that will listen to reason — let him be reasoned with, but it is the weaponed arm of the patriot that alone can prevail against battalioned despotism.

"Then, my Lord, I do not condemn the use of arms as immoral, nor do I conceive it to be profane to say that the King of Heaven bestows His benediction upon those who unsheath the sword in the hour of a nation's peril.

"Abhor the sword? No, my lord, for in the passes of the Tyrol, it cut to pieces the banner of the Bavarian.

"Abhor the sword? No, my lord, for at its blow, a great nation started from the waters of the Atlantic, and the crippled colony sprang into the attitude of a proud republic — prosperous, limitless, and invincible!"

By now the audience was cheering wildly. John O'Connell stood up. "I cannot permit you to continue," he told Meagher. "This is not in keeping with the purposes and methods of the Repeal Association, nor with the peaceful principles advocated by my father. It is not part of our plan."

Shouts arose from all parts of the audience. "Then let's have our own plan." "Let's walk out of here." "Hurrah for the sword!" "Hurrah for Mitchel and Meagher!"

The disorder ended only when Meagher walked from the hall, followed by hundreds of sympathizers. The break of Young Ireland with the Repeal Association was now complete.

By now the potato crop had failed again and the poor of Ireland everywhere lay starving. Meanwhile the English landlords, drawing great wealth from lands which their ancestors had stolen from the Irish, and frequently not living in Ireland themselves — and therefore not seeing matters firsthand — were shipping more than enough wheat — they called it "corn" — out of Ireland to feed everybody well. The land was tilled, the seed planted, the crop harvested by the Irish. The result was that while Ireland itself produced enough food for its people, its people starved and the absentee landlords grew richer.

With armed revolution throughout Europe, the *Nation* finally followed the *United Irishmen* in advocating revolutionary instead of peaceful solutions for Ireland's troubles. Irishmen all over the island read these two weekly papers and were making up their minds that Ireland must prepare to gain her liberty by resolute hearts rather than resolutions, and, if need be, by armed rather than extended hands. Bonfires lighted by patriots blazed on the Irish hills, and tricolor flags — the symbols of revolution — everywhere flew from the windows of the Confederate clubrooms.

In Dublin, public meetings were held to congratulate the French on their successful revolution, and a delegation was sent to Paris to tell the people of France and the government how entirely the people of Ireland rejoiced in the French success.

At the last of these meetings, Meagher said, "The time has come for every Irishman to speak out. I declare myself the enemy of the government. Let the demand for the reconstruction of the nationality of Ireland be constitutionally made. If nothing comes of this, then up with the barricades and invoke the God of Battles."

To friends of Ireland this was a summons to take up arms. The English government well understood what such talk promised. Anticipating it, they sent a reporter to take shorthand notes of the meeting and immediately arrested Meagher and William O'Brien, the chairman, charging them with sedition. Although these men were quickly freed, the English did not forget what Meagher had said and, as we shall see, such brave but rash words almost cost him his life.

Other brave but rash Irishmen were equally outspoken. John Mitchel wrote in the *United Irishmen* of March 18, "We await attack. We shall not provoke the shedding of blood; but if blood be shed, we shall see the end of it." On March 20, although there were 12,000 English troops in Dublin, a great outdoor meeting of 12,000 to 15,000 unarmed Irishmen was held. Again Meagher spoke; and two days later, he talked from the window of the council rooms of the Confederation.

"They have indicted me for sedition," said Mitchel, "but I tell them that I intend to commit high treason."

And Meagher said, "I shall speak to the judge, the jury, and the prosecuting underlings of this thuglike government. I shall tell them to their faces that I have spoken sedition, and that I glory in it. One circumstance alone shall stop me — my death."

Meagher and the other members of the Irish delegation arrived in Paris toward the end of March and learned firsthand from the French how they had overthrown the king. While they were away, the patriots of Dublin, which was the seat of the English government in Ireland, were preparing to expel the English. The people of Milan had forced the Austrian garrison to leave their city, and the citizens of Dublin believed that they could do as much to the English garrison.

Two days after Meagher left for France, for the first time the Confederation Clubs marched in full military fashion to a huge mass meeting in the Dublin music hall, while thousands cheered along the way and cheering crowds gathered around the building itself. Mitchel rose and addressed the audience. When he finished, a well-known Dublin hardware manufacturer handed him a pike.

"Mr. Mitchel," said the manufacturer, "I put into your hands a pike. This is the traditional weapon of the Irish peasant."

"It is still a usable weapon," said Mitchel, holding the pike, with its pointed steel head on a long wooden shaft, "and I tell you Irishmen that within a week pikes will be publicly exposed for sale in Dublin."

Pikes *were* openly on sale in the stores of Dublin within the week, and the government in Ireland and England felt that existing law was comparatively powerless. To meet the threat, a bill called the Treason and Felony Act, which put teeth into the law, was passed by the English parliament. This bill provided that certain seditious or disloyal offenses could now be punished by transportation for life. Transportation meant exile to empty British possessions halfway around the globe. Australia, New Zealand, and Tasmania were among the places to which prisoners were transported. Nor could a prisoner, before he was tried, demand the right to be released on bail so that he would have the means and liberty to prepare his case. This bill, passed in April, 1848, made nearly every speech delivered by the Irish Confederates, and every article published in the *Nation,* an act of treason. It also exposed the speaker or writer to a life of terrible punishment. But it took more than this threat to silence men like Meagher, Mitchel, and O'Brien.

So greatly did the English fear rebellion at this moment that the Queen and the royal family left London for the safety of the Isle of Wight. It should be added in all fairness that at the start of the nineteenth century there were many very bad conditions, political, social, economic, and religious, in England itself; and that while patriotic Irishmen were working and fighting for their liberties and for justice, many good Englishmen sympathized with them, and were waging the same or similar battles, not only for the Irish but for themselves. Although the government of England was far less democratic than it is today, at least England had its own government and many Englishmen had some part in it. Peaceful means could therefore be more successful in England than in Ireland, and therefore the English did not find it necessary, as did the Irish, to fall back on armed rebellion.

After he returned from Paris, Meagher set himself to the task of arming and equipping the members of the Grattan Club, of which he was president. While the less prosperous clubs of the Irish Confederation armed themselves with eight-foot pikes, prosperous clubs like Meagher's were supplied with a serviceable rifle and its equipment.

"But I can't afford to buy a rifle and all the other things that are needed," more than one club member told Meagher.

"Well now, I have some money in my pocket to

help along in just such cases as yours," was Meagher's invariable answer. The money came from Meagher's personal funds.

Meanwhile, loyal Irishmen, who had been discharged or had deserted from the British army, risked being transported by drilling Irish recruits in out-of-the-way barns or cellars. To disarm the Irish, the English Lord Lieutenant made secret plans for a general search for arms in Dublin. He proposed to station soldiers at street crossings to stop people from entering or leaving certain districts where it was likely that arms were hidden. While the streets were blocked, squads of English soldiers would search the houses. The plan was abandoned when the English learned that the news of it had leaked out to the Irish revolutionary clubs.

When the Dublin clubs were organized and armed, Meagher and other patriots began a tour of Ireland to visit clubs outside the capitol and to stir up revolutionary sentiment. Tempers in Ireland ran high when, in the middle of May, John Mitchell was arrested for treason. Mitchel's arrest had been expected, because the Treason-Felony Act had been specially designed to silence him.

Mitchel was confined in Newgate Prison, the "Bastille" of Dublin. News went around to the clubs that, to free Mitchel, Newgate Prison should be torn down stone by stone, if necessary. Pikes were taken out from hiding and the blades polished and honed to razor sharpness. To escort Mitchel to the courts of law, sixteen Dublin clubs marched to the prison and a near riot followed. By now it was clear that it would be difficult to prevent open warfare in Ireland. All patriots anxiously awaited the "word."

The "word" was the signal to rise and to use their arms in an attempt to throw off their English masters. But the leaders did not give the word. They did not feel that the Irish were as yet ready. After the complaints against Mitchel were determined he was returned to prison. In the midst of this tense atmosphere, the trials of O'Brien and Meagher began.

O'Brien's trial for sedition was held first, and O'Brien was released because the jury could not agree on a verdict. Meagher's trial on the same charge began on Tuesday, March 16, and had the same ending.

That evening about nine o'clock, the clubs of Dublin paraded through the city to celebrate the release of O'Brien and Meagher, and to make a demonstration before Newgate Prison in honor of Mitchel. Tremendous crowds swarmed out to greet and applaud the marchers.

To prevent such demonstrations in the future, Lord Clarendon, the English governor, issued a proclamation. Thousands of these notices were posted throughout Dublin.

"So His Excellency is posting notices denying us the right to assemble peaceably and express our feelings," O'Brien thought. "Well, two can play at the game of posting notices. I'll post a few myself."

That evening, next to every notice of the governor's, a second notice was posted. It told the citizens of Dublin to stand by their rights and it dared the English government to interfere. It was apparent that both sides were looking for trouble and that unless one or the other backed down — which was not likely, since both were angry — sooner or later there would be a fight.

Lord Clarendon also ordered the Dublin police to blockade the streets leading to the Confederation's council rooms. Although on the following Sunday, March 21, 1848, four hundred policemen stood shoulder to shoulder to block the way of the clubs as they marched up, they broke ranks to permit them to pass through to attend an open-air meeting called to consider ways and means of seeing that Mitchel was given a fair trial.

The members of the Confederation anticipated that the English government would "pack" Mitchel's jury. To try Mitchel, the English government wanted only jurors who were sympathetic to the English rule in Ireland and unsympathetic to the Irish revolutionaries.

While the announced purpose of the meeting was to protest against the likely packing of Mitchel's jury, and to hint that serious consequences might follow an unfair trial, many Irishmen felt that if Mitchel were convicted an attempt by force should be made to rescue him. Some leaders of the Irish Confederation shared this view.

"Of course we've got to rescue Mitchel," they argued. "If we let the English convict him and transport him to a penal colony, some of our less courageous club members are going to get weak-kneed. They may even quit."

To see whether the Dublin clubs could muster

strength enough to attempt a rescue, Meagher and O'Gorman made a tour of the city.

"It's hopeless, boys," they reported to the Council on their return. "We don't have the ghost of a chance of rescuing Mitchel by force."

It took courage to announce this conclusion. But Meagher honestly believed then — although he later changed his mind — that an attempt to rescue Mitchel would harm the cause.

While it was clear that Mitchel was guilty of breaking a law that most Irishmen hated as a bad law, it seemed necessary to the British government that an example should be made of him. For this reason, as the Irish patriots had anticipated, the jury was packed and Mitchel was doomed. When the trial was over, he was asked if he had anything to say as he faced the judge. Meagher was among the spectators.

"I have been tried by a packed jury," Mitchel said, "by the jury of a partisan sheriff, by a packed jury obtained by a juggle. That is the reason why I object to the sentence being passed upon me."

After Mitchel received his sentence, to be transported beyond the seas for fourteen years, he spoke again.

"Neither the jury, nor the judges, nor any other man in this court presumes to imagine that it is a criminal who stands in this dock. The Roman who saw his hand burning to ashes promised the tyrant that three hundred should follow in his enterprise. Can I not promise for one, or two, or three, aye for hundreds?"

Here Mitchel pointed to Meagher, Reilly, and Martin. Immediately voices in the courtroom cried out, "Yes, Mitchel, promise for me." "And for me." "Promise for me."

Frightened, the officers seized Mitchel and pushed him through a doorway to the rear to be dragged off in irons to the steamer *Sheerwater*, which was waiting to receive him. Then the judges gathered up their robes and fled, while the sheriff escorted Meagher and other friends of Mitchel from the building.

Even though the majority of the Dublin Confederates were greatly disappointed at the action of the Council in not permitting them to try to rescue Mitchel by force, their enthusiasm for the cause of Irish freedom grew greater than ever. During the next six months their numbers doubled, and the program to supply them with arms was equally successful. Throughout Ireland the deportation of Mitchel did much to unite all Irishmen and to convince them that they must organize and arm. Everywhere blacksmiths working at forges guarded by sentinel-patriots hammered iron bars into pikes.

But the members of the Confederation Council were not fooled by the fact that they were still out of jail. "We know what's happening," they said to one another. "The government is playing cat and mouse with us. Any time His Lordship wants a fresh victim, we will be arrested."

"We understand," they agreed. "We'll get what Mitchel got, an unfair trial and deportation — or worse. We're living on borrowed time."

In spite of the danger over their heads, however, they refused to give the word to begin the open armed revolt. They knew full well that until the Irish patriots were sufficiently well prepared to fight with some chance of winning, it was murder and suicide to provoke or even risk an open fight.

"We'll have no more street parades," they decided. "Unless we order them ourselves."

A new Council was elected. The leaders of the old Council who knew one another well and trusted one another to death whispered: "There's a leak somewhere to the English. Someone of our friends must be a traitor and a spy. How else would they find out what we think and plan in secret?"

Meanwhile, a few of the Confederation leaders had met and decided that they would secretly send representatives to other countries to obtain money and arms and to recruit officers. To confuse the English they would also organize a revolt among the many loyal Irishmen who lived in England. John Mitchel's brother was one of the two delegates sent to America. A few weeks later, another agent was sent to France.

"This won't do," said one member of the Council. "Our two American delegates are not accustomed to addressing public meetings. I think that Meagher should follow them to America. We need someone who can present the cause of Ireland to large audiences there."

"Will you go?" the Committee asked Meagher.

"I'm willing to go," Meagher agreed, "provided I can return to Ireland before the harvest is ripe."

Harvest time was set for the armed uprising. Crops in the barns would assist in supplying the revolutionists with food. Meanwhile, patriotic Irish Protestants had organized the Protestant Repeal Association, and two new newspapers, the *Irish Tribune* and the *Irish Felon,* began publication.

But the English government got word of the proposed uprising and was not of the mind to sit idly by while the Irish patriots picked their time. If revolution was unavoidable, the government felt the leaders at least could be kept from participating. First to be arrested and imprisoned in Newgate Prison in Dublin in July were the editors. In the trials that followed, all were deported except Richard Williams. Williams, a poet and journalist, probably was acquitted because his Protestant lawyer quoted his poem, "The Sister of Charity," with such feeling as to touch the heart and conscience of at least one member of the packed jury.

At the time of the editors' arrest, most of the other Confederate leaders were absent from Dublin, working for the revolution. Meagher was making a tour of inspection of the clubs in the County of Munster. After visiting Cork, Meagher hurried to Cahermoyle and thence went to Rathkeale. Having addressed the inhabitants of Rathkeale from the window of his hotel room, he went to Waterford.

On Tuesday, July 11, Captain Gunn knocked on the door of Mayor Meagher's house. With him was Constable Hughes. "Is Mr. Thomas Francis Meagher within?" Gunn asked.

The officers were shown inside. Meagher was waiting for them. "I am Thomas Francis Meagher."

"I bear a warrant for your arrest," said Captain Gunn.

"Upon what charge?"

"On the charge of using seditious language in speaking to the people of Rathkeale."

As the news of Meagher's arrest quickly spread through Waterford, church bells were rung, the whole populace poured into the streets, and everyone talked about a rescue. Before Meagher could leave the house, a crowd had gathered.

Meagher stepped to the window. The crowd was angry. Fists were raised. Faces showed that the mood was ugly. Shouts of threats against the English became a sullen roar. Meagher raised his hand and waited. When he could be heard, he said, quietly, "My friends, please do not do anything rash by attempting to rescue me by force."

The people in the streets would not listen. Neither would the officers take him away while the mob threatened. Prominent Waterford citizens came to the Meagher home, and English soldiers. An hour after his first appeal, Meagher again appeared at the window and pleaded: "Please disperse. Trouble now will only injure the cause of Ireland. Bloodshed will bring trouble."

Someone crowded into the parlor and whispered to Meagher: "The clubs from all the towns in the neighborhood are preparing to march upon Waterford to rescue you."

Meagher acted quickly. "Send two messengers to see that the order is countermanded," he said.

Four hours after Meagher's arrest, a chaise drew up to carry him away and again Meagher pleaded with the crowd not to act rashly. The crowd quieted down and, escorted by the soldiers, Meagher was taken away toward the Carlow railroad station to proceed by train to Dublin.

As the procession neared the bridge across the Suir River the feelings of the people broke loose and men crowded the doors of the chaise.

"For God's sake, sir, give us the word," they begged.

Meagher spoke from the step. "My good friends, I told you at my father's house that violence now would result in the useless shedding of Irish blood. I order you to go home peaceably. I will not give you the word!"

This refusal was met by shouts more sorrowful than angry: "You will regret it, sir. And, it's all your own fault, sir."

Some of the mob even cut the reins and traces of the horses, so that the chaise was unable to move for a full hour until the harness was replaced. Although Meagher's lieutenants in the crowd tried to control the Irish patriots, the crowd grew more and more unruly and stones began to fly.

At the bridge the procession was delayed by a barricade formed by two immense planks. Amid a shower of stones Meagher left the chaise, took off his hat, and begged the people to be faithful to the promise they had given him and remove the barricade. At the Kilkenny gate the crowd allowed one party of dragoons to pass and then shut and barred the gate, so that the escort was divided. When they began to shower stones and a bloody riot threatened, Meagher clambered to the roof of the chaise.

"Open the gate," he ordered. "And all of you desist.

This rioting will lead only to trouble and useless bloodshed."

Sullenly the mob drew aside and allowed the gate to be opened.

In Dublin, Meagher was placed under heavy bail and then released. His trial was set for the next Limerick assizes.

Chapter III

THE THUNDER OF
REVOLUTIONARY DRUMS

MEAGHER'S arrest neither frightened him nor made him more careful. He and Michael Doheny had ordered a great outdoor meeting to be held at the high hill of Slievenamon on July 16, 1848. This hill, which rises two thousand feet above the plain of Femhan, is rich with Irish history.

On the morning of the meeting, long before the time for its opening, streams of people crowded into the nearby towns and flowed along the highways leading to the rallying place. Though the day became hot and the climb was difficult, the patriots trudged up the steep ascent. The military and police at Garrick-on-Suir had been under arms in the barracks, looking for trouble. Nevertheless, the clubs gathered on schedule at the town's green and, to the cheers of the old folks, marched to the meeting place. The top of the hill was black with onlookers when the first of the clubs appeared. By 2 p.m. 50,000 determined men had gathered to hear the leaders.

Others spoke. Michael Doheny dwelt at length on the necessity for the people to arm themselves by every available means. Finally Meagher stood before the cheering multitude. He was wearing a green cap with a gold band and a splendid tricolor sash — the symbols of Irish patriotism and revolution.

He told the immense audience: "I am here to report of nothing [loud cheers], but to dare the government to do something worse than arrest me. I felt that I lived in a land of slavery, and that if God gave me intellect, it ought to be employed for the country. It is my ambition to decorate these hills with the flag of my country.

"A scourge came from God. The potato was smitten, but your fields waved with golden grain. To your lips it was forbidden fruit. The ships came and bore it away. The fact is plain, that this land, which is yours by nature, and by God's gift, is not yours by the law of the land. There were bayonets, therefore, between the people and their rightful food."

"This is open rebellion, even if it is the truth," his friendly listeners agreed.

The "Castle," the name which the Irish applied to

the English government, the Lord Lieutenant who represented the Queen, and the fortified palace in Dublin which represented the royal authority — shared this opinion. It could not permit its authority to be sneered at in this fashion. And so it set about to disarm and disband the Irish patriotic clubs. Newspapers with English sympathies had been urging this step for weeks. The Slievenamon gathering forced the Castle's hand.

Some towns, cities, and districts such as Tipperary had already been quarantined. Those who lived in quarantined districts, and did not carry special permits, were ordered to surrender their arms and ammunition within four days. If they failed to do so and were caught, the penalty was a year's imprisonment at hard labor. The districts now quarantined included places where the clubs were strongest: Dublin, Cork, Waterford, and Drogheda.

The proclamations posted by the government in public places bore the English coat of arms: a lion and a unicorn. In Dublin, Meagher had seen the success of Smith O'Brien's counterproclamations. He told the printer: "Print proclamations for me telling the club members to disregard the commands of the Castle. They should maintain their club organizations and wait for orders from us."

"What shall I use for an emblem instead of the English coat of arms?" the printer asked.

"Use the emblem of old Ireland, the harp on the green flag."

When the men of the quarantine towns and districts saw Meagher's proclamation posted next to the governor's, they took courage. Their spirits mounted higher when Charles Duffey and John Marten from their Dublin cells wrote signed articles for the patriotic papers, pleading with the Irish not to surrender their arms.

Even before this display of courage by the leaders, the patriotic clubs in the quarantined places had anticipated this advice and were meeting to find out how many men and guns they could count on, and whether they should beat the government to the punch by calling for a general uprising in Dublin.

Delegates returned from touring Ireland, to report that the clubs were ready; and on Saturday, July 22, an executive council of five was chosen by the club delegates to exercise supreme control over the revolutionary movement. Meagher was a member of this council.

It was clear to everybody now that open rebellion was on the point of breaking out. To strengthen the Irish government against the Irish patriotic leaders, the British parliament passed a bill suspending *habeas corpus* in Ireland. *Habeas corpus* is a law which compels a government to bring an arrested person into court and to make public the reason for his arrest.

Irish patriots hoped that when their rebellion began, the revolutionary government of France would, if necessary, send the French army and navy to their aid. To arrange for this help, a secret emissary of the Committee was dispatched to Paris.

Another representative of the Committee, Thomas Darcy McGee, was sent to Belfast, the most important city in North Ireland and a great industrial center and seaport on the Clyde River.

"When you arrive in Belfast," McGee was told, "hide until you hear from us that the uprising has begun. Then come out and call upon the Irish population to attack the English garrison in Belfast."

McGee listened carefully.

"When you have overpowered the English, seize two or three ships in the Clyde, put two thousand or more loyal Irishmen on them, and compel their crews to get under way. Sail around the north of Ireland and land the reinforcements at Sligo. From there march to join Meagher and the clubs in Tipperary."

While no one could question the patriotism or courage of the men who planned it, this was clearly an impractical scheme. So were most of the other plans. The only defense that can be made for schemes of this kind is the fact that the schemers were young, inexperienced, enthusiastic, and filled with indignation at the sight of the Irish sufferings. Further, they did not ask their followers to take chances which they refused to take themselves.

After McGee had left, Meagher went upstairs in the clubroom with John Dillon, another member of the executive committee, and took from the wall a large map of Ireland.

"We'll take this along into the country," Meagher said, "and use it to guide our military movements."

If experienced military men had been preparing to put into operation a complicated plan to strike at an enemy, they would have been careful at this point to make sure that the campaign had been carefully thought through, that it was clearly understood by everyone concerned, and that each man understood his own assignment. They would have known who was to give and who was to take orders, and who was to command if one of them was killed or captured. They would have made plans to keep in contact so that they would operate as one. But Meagher and his friends failed to make such wise provisions, and so as soon as the plotters took to the field, the poorly planned, desperate venture began to fall apart.

Meagher himself said that he sent out orders to the presidents of the Dublin clubs. After telling them what was happening, he instructed them to hold themselves ready to rise. When they heard that Meagher and his friends had actually struck the first blow, they should rise and barricade the streets of Dublin. By then, Meagher believed, the Dublin garrison would have marched off to join English troops in putting down the revolt in the south of Ireland.

Meagher had told the Dublin clubs that he would send orders to the secretary of the Committee, who remained behind in Dublin. The secretary would give orders to the presidents of the clubs. This was a poor arrangement. If the secretary lost his nerve, or was killed or arrested, there was nobody to give orders, and the chain of command would break down. As it turned out, the secretary of the Committee was a good but timid man. And so the Dublin clubs did not get the orders to rise and therefore did not strike.

Meagher and his friend Dillon could not have guessed this weakness in their plans as they caught the

8 o'clock train leaving Dublin. They were going south to begin the revolution.

On the train they sat near an Englishman — a very stiff, cold, sober gentleman with red whiskers and a florid complexion. The Englishman had been reading about the suspension of the Habeas Corpus Act. He folded the paper with a satisfied look. "The government has done the thing at last," he puffed. "Should have been done a long time ago. The Whigs have given the scoundrels too much rope. But they'll hang themselves — I swear it — they will."

Dillon burst out laughing. Two or three passengers recognized the two Irish revolutionaries but little suspected their exciting business.

At Loghlenstown, seven miles from Dublin, Dillon and Meagher left the train and waited at the roadside for the public coach. Because the Dublin police were checking on their movements, seats had been reserved for them in Dublin in the name of Charles Hart, who accompanied them. The coach stop was under a spreading tree; and, in the misty twilight gloom, rain dripped on the two silent men. Each was wrapped in his own thoughts. They well understood their desperate business.

Correctly, Meagher sensed that the task was beyond their strength to accomplish, yet he felt that he could not retreat. He said, "The leading men of the Confederation were bound to go out and offer the country the sword and banner of revolt, whatever the consequences to themselves."

At 9 o'clock the coach came up, Dillon and Meagher said good-by to Hart, the guard sang out "all right," and in a couple of seconds the conspirators were under way. For eight hours they rode through the night, and a little after 5 the next morning they arrived at Enniscorthy. The morning was bitter cold, in spite of the fact that a bright sun was already melting the thin frost and turning golden the gray haze over the Slaney River. Leaving the coach here, they rented a buggy for Ballinkeele.

While the horse was being harnessed, Meagher sat down before the fire and read the latest issue of the *Felon*. The streets outside were empty and silent. The hotel itself was quiet; in the stable yard the chickens still slept, and the old dog snored comfortably beside the kitchen fire. The editor asked: "Who will draw the first blood for Ireland? Who will win a wreath that shall be green forever?"

Smith O'Brien had preceded them to Bellinkeele on an inspection tour. They found him there.

"What do you propose to do?" O'Brien asked.

"We have three choices," Dillon told him. "We can allow ourselves to be arrested. We can escape. Or we can give the signal for insurrection."

"I am in favor of giving the signal to rise," said O'Brien.

"We have already made up our minds to do so," they assured him.

As the three drove to Enniscorthy, they discussed plans. Although they were in Wexford, they did not think it would be well to begin the revolt there. The clubs had not enrolled many Wexford men. No, they would have to commence where people were organized and ready for revolution. Waterford and Kilkenny in Tipperary looked like likely places. Finally, they began to talk about Kilkenny.

"The town of Kilkenny is inland," Meagher observed. "The English won't be able to get their war steamers, gunboats, and floating batteries up the Nore River."

"Kilkenny County touches borders with the three best fighting counties in Ireland," O'Brien agreed. "There's Wexford on the east, Waterford on the south, and Tipperary on the west."

Dillon added more reasons for favoring Kilkenny. The town of Kilkenny alone contained from three to five thousand armed Confederates. Its narrow streets made easy the erection of barricades. The barracks of the English garrison lay across the river from the town and the bridge could be demolished or defended. Even more important, the railroad from Dublin was completed only to Bagnalstown, leaving a gap of fourteen miles of narrow coach road to Kilkenny. This wound between thickets, high walls, and brambled fences, and thus provided many ideal spots at which to ambush English forces, rushed from the garrisons of Dublin and Newbridge.

In view of these advantages, it was not difficult for the three to come to a decision: they would begin the armed attack on the English at the town of Kilkenny.

On July 25, Smith O'Brien, Meagher, and other leaders were at Carrick-on-Suir, up the river some fifteen miles from Meagher's native Waterford. Clubmen from the town and country swarmed in the streets.

"The day has come at last!" the crowds cheered.

Meagher himself described the scene: "A torrent of human beings, rushing through lanes and narrow streets; surging and boiling against the white basements that hemmed it in; with sounds of wrath, vengeance, and defiance; clenched hands, waving to and fro, with wildest confusion in the air; eyes, red with rage and desperation; long tresses of hair streaming in the roaring wind of voices; wild, half-stifled, passionate, frantic prayers of hope; invocation in sobs; challenges to the foe; curses on the red flag; scornful, exulting defiance of death; all wild as the winter gusts at sea, yet as black and fearful, too; this is what I then beheld — these sounds I heard — such the dream which passed before me!

"It was the REVOLUTION, if we had accepted it.

"Why it was not accepted, I fear, I cannot with sufficient accuracy explain."

It is difficult to explain confusion.

When the news circulated through the Dublin clubs that the leaders had taken to the field to begin the revolt, hopes ran high. The Dublin men were ready.

But, as we have seen, they had been told to await instructions from the Executive Committee, so that the actual fight would first begin in South Ireland. The Dublin garrison would then be weakened by the loss of the men sent to Kilkenny. Then it would be easier to seize Dublin.

When Meagher's messenger arrived, he could not find the Council's secretary. Secretary Halpin was out of town. He had either misunderstood Meagher's instructions or he lost his nerve. The reason for his absence made no practical difference. He had gone to Tipperary. In his absence no one transmitted Meagher's orders. And so the presidents of the Dublin clubs hesitated until it was too late to act. The Dublin clubs built no barricades, stormed no citadels, and fired not one of the dearly bought guns. And the pikes remained to rust in hiding.

Out in the field, conditions were as confused. Smith O'Brien at Carrick found the countryside trembling with excitement, the aroused people crying to be led against the English. Suddenly the fervor cooled.

Perhaps it was a spy in the hire of the English who began to whisper; perhaps it was timidity, or common sense.

"We citizens of Carrick are expected to stand all by ourselves against the English. As punishment the government will destroy both our city and ourselves."

The rumor spread. The common people grew frightened.

"You may stay overnight," certain important citizens of Carrick-on-Suir told O'Brien and his companions, "but you'll have to leave in the morning. It's too much of a risk we take of angering the English if you remain here beyond that."

"I'd like to find out who started this rumor," O'Brien said.

The terror of Carrick-on-Suir spread to the surrounding towns and countryside. When Meagher heard the story, he gave orders: "The clubs in the neighborhood of Carrick are to march to Carrick tomorrow."

"Will you join them, Mr. Meagher?" he was asked.

"I will join them. I am going to Waterford immediately. There I will take command of a thousand men. They have sworn to follow me, at a moment's notice, wherever I choose to lead them."

When Meagher arrived in Waterford, he looked up the leaders of the thousand shock troops.

"We cannot go to Carrick with you, without Father Tracy's permission," they told Meagher. Father Tracy was the principal adviser of the Waterford clubs.

"But where is Father Tracy?" Meagher asked impatiently.

"We don't know," the Waterford men told him.

Convinced that they did not know, Meagher set out in the dark of the night to look for him. After searching in every likely place, he could not find him. Nor could anyone give him a clue to Father Tracy's whereabouts.

Finally Meagher could wait no longer, and all alone and in despair, without his thousand sturdy fighting men, he set out in the darkness to return to Carrick-on-Suir. The confusion that night was such that a great portion of the patriots of his native city did not know that Meagher had returned to lead them in person in beginning the open revolt.

Meagher ordered no one to fire a gun or thrust a pike. Nor did he himself draw a sword. His experience was typical of the uprising as a whole. It failed before it fairly started.

And so the Young Ireland movement ended. Meagher later insisted that the defeat of 1848 was "not the defeat of a whole people. It was nothing more than the rout of a few peasants, hastily collected, badly armed, half-starved, and miserably clad. The country did not turn out." And the country, therefore, should not be blamed. It would be fair to say that because of a series of blunders the movement fell to pieces. Secretary Halpin's confusion or loss of nerve prevented the men of Dublin from attacking the Dublin garrison, and Father Tracy's absence deprived Meagher of the thousand men who were to be the nucleus of the army of the rising.

The Young Ireland movement did not have the support of all the bishops and priests, or the full support of some who were friendly.

Meagher said: "As a body they were opposed to us from the day of the Secession down to the very day on which the suspension of the Habeas Corpus Act was announced by express in Dublin. In not joining us, therefore, in the field — in not exhorting the people to take up arms — nay, in setting themselves against the few who rallied around us, and warning them to their homes — in all this they did not act treacherously, they acted simply with strict consistency."

Meagher believed that they were in error in so acting. It is hard to agree with him. The clergy of Ireland was not lacking in patriotism. It was long on common sense. It probably did not want to see peasants armed with pikes mowed down by soldiers armed with guns. Whatever the secondary causes of the failure may have been, there can be no doubt that the main cause was a "lack of organization among the people selected by the leaders to inaugurate the movement" and an "utter lack of military knowledge among those leaders themselves."

When it became clear that it was not possible to rally any considerable body of armed revolutionists in southern Ireland, and that the plan to seize Dublin was hopelessly stalled, the leaders asked themselves what they should do next.

Someone suggested that since they did not seem to be able to begin a revolution by a simultaneous uprising, each of them should take a separate command, raise the green flag, and see what he could do by himself.

Meagher opposed this plan. He knew that the English would pick off the little independent rebel bands, one by one. "United we stand; divided we fall."

Finally the leaders agreed to separate and to try to make their individual escapes from Ireland.

After amazing adventures by land and sea, some of them managed to evade the British police and soldiers and the sailors of Her Majesty's navy to find refuge in Europe or America.

Others were arrested. Meagher was among the latter group. On August 12, in the company of several patriots, he was taken prisoner near Rathgannon and immediately conveyed to Kilmainham Prison in Dublin. The charge against him and the other prisoners was high treason. If guilty, the penalty was death by hanging.

With the revolution smashed and the English in full control of the country, Meagher could not expect a friendly jury. Now he was in for it. And he knew it.

Chapter IV

STRONG WINDS TO
DISTANT PLACES

ON SEPTEMBER 18, Meagher and the other prisoners charged with high treason were taken by railroad to Thurles and from there by coach to Clomnel. A special commission, opening on the twenty-first, was to try them. With failure behind them and conviction and death ahead, the prisoners joked and laughed on the journey. They were young and contemptuous of English authority. Nevertheless, they had little but death to look forward to. Terrible though the wrongs of Ireland had been, and great the justification for revolt, it was clear that they had violated English law. It was equally clear that they would not be given a fair trial.

Smith O'Brien was tried first, before a carefully "packed" jury, all members of which were of English descent. When the verdict of guilty was brought in by the jury, O'Brien was standing in the felon's box.

"Smith O'Brien, do you have anything to say why the sentence of death should not be passed on you?"

O'Brien's voice was calm and clear: "I am perfectly satisfied with the consciousness that I have performed my duty to my country; that I have done only that which, in my opinion, it was the duty of every Irishman to have done; and I am prepared to abide the consequences of having performed my duty to my native land. Proceed with your sentence."

The sentence was death by hanging, with savage indignities to the body.

On Monday, October 16, 1848, the trial of Thomas Francis Meagher for high treason against the government of Her Majesty, Victoria, Queen of England, Scotland, and Ireland, began in Clomnel Courthouse.

Outside the streets were thronged. The whole town and the surrounding countryside had turned out to witness the excitement. The courthouse itself was jammed to overflowing. When Meagher was brought into the courtroom, all eyes turned on him.

His friends whispered, "He's a cool one."

"Yes, look at the way he's dressed for the hanging."

Meagher's clothes showed his usual fastidious taste: plain black frock coat, black silk stock, and a light-colored waistcoat. As he took his seat in the prisoner's dock, he looked around the courtroom with the easy composure of a man in the midst of friends. All saw that he wore a large gold ring. They could not know that the stone in it contained a miniature portrait of his friend, John Mitchel.

The court asked: "Are you guilty or not guilty?"

In a clear, firm voice, Meagher replied, "Not guilty."

Then he continued: "My lords, previous to the jury being sworn, I respectfully beg leave to say a few words. I desire to protest against the construction of the panel from which the jury by which I am to be tried has been selected. Personally, I care not whether I am to be tried by Protestants or Roman Catholics. I feel that my cause, my honor, my liberty, my life are as safe in the hands of a jury composed exclusively of Protestants as they would be of a jury composed exclusively of Roman Catholics. But as a matter of principle I feel myself called upon to protest against the system by which, in a Catholic country, only eighteen Roman Catholics are returned upon a panel of nearly three hundred jurors."

This speech was followed by loud cheering and hand clapping and the stamping of feet in the galleries.

Meagher had instructed his lawyer not to challenge the panel or selection of jurors. The trial of Smith O'Brien proved that the government did not want to give the prisoner a chance to escape through a jury that was divided. Meagher anticipated that the jury would be packed. And it was. Although one of the jurors was a Catholic, all of them bore English names.

The formal charges made against Meagher were

two: he had levied war against the Queen, and he had plotted her death. The court found Meagher guilty on both counts.

Two of his associates, McManus and O'Donohue, were next tried on the same charges and found guilty. When the three prisoners were brought to the bar on October 23 for judgment, the judge asked them if they had anything to say. Meagher spoke for the three.

"My lords, it is my intention to say a few words only. With my country I leave my memory — my sentiments — my acts — proudly feeling that they require no vindication from me this day. A jury of my countrymen have found me guilty. Influenced by the charge of the Lord Chief Justice, they could have found no other verdict.

"What of the charge? I would earnestly beseech of you, my lord, when the passions and prejudices of this hour have passed away, to appeal to your conscience.

"You may deem this language unbecoming in me, and perhaps it may seal my fate. But I am here to speak the truth, whatever it may cost. I am here to regret nothing I have ever done — to retract nothing I have ever said. I am here to crave with no lying lip the life I consecrate to my country. Far from it; even here — here, where the thief, the libertine, and murderers have left their footprints in the dust; here where the shadows of death surround me; even here, encircled by these terrors, the hope which had beckoned me to the perilous sea upon which I have been wrecked, still consoles, animates, enraptures me.

"Judged by the law of England, I knew this crime entails the penalty of death; but the history of Ireland explains this crime, and justifies it. Judged by that history, I am no criminal, we are no criminals, we deserve no punishment. Judged by that history, the treason of which I stand convicted loses all its guilt, is sanctified as a duty, will be ennobled as a sacrifice.

"Pronounce then the sentence which the law directs. I trust I shall be prepared to meet its execution. I hope that I will be able to appear before a higher tribunal where a Judge of infinite goodness, as well as justice, will preside, and where, my lords, many of the judgments of this world will be reversed."

Tradition has it that Meagher added: "This is our first offense, but not our last. If you will be easy with us this once, we promise on our word as gentlemen to try to do better the next time."

The judge then pronounced sentence on each of them: "The sentence is that you, Thomas Francis Meagher, be taken from hence to the place from whence you came, and be thence drawn on a hurdle to the place of execution, and there be hanged by the neck until you are dead; and that afterward your head shall be severed from your body, and your body divided into four quarters to be disposed of as Her Majesty shall think fit, and may God have mercy on your soul."

By now the newspapers of the world were following the trial and, with the eyes of civilized people everywhere upon her, Queen Victoria three days later commuted the death penalty to "transportation" for life. This new sentence was read to the prisoners on October 26 in Clonmel jail. Later they were transferred to Kilmainham jail in Dublin on their way to

Richmond Bridewell. There they remained for eight months while certain well-meaning friends, without their consent, raised legal questions on their behalf. Finally, on July 9, 1849, the deportation order came and was read to the prisoners.

The next morning, at 7 o'clock, off the Waterford coast, Meagher looked north over the blue waves of St. George's Channel toward the estuary of the Suir. Never again, except in his dreams, would he gaze upon the river of his childhood haunts. He wrote in his diary at that hour: "Will no one come out to hail me from Dunmore? I pass by, and my own people know nothing of it."

Events for him and for the other prisoners had moved rapidly during the preceding twenty-four hours. At half past ten a police van, escorted by fifty mounted police armed with pistols and carbines, had pulled up within the wall of the prison. Shortly after, three troops of dragoons had arrived. The government was taking no chances that the prisoners might break away or be rescued.

An hour later, amid tears, waving of handkerchiefs, and farewells, the van with the prisoners inside pulled away at a rapid pace for the harbor. There Meagher saw artillerymen standing next to loaded guns and colonels of all branches of Her Majesty's service.

He nudged McManus and said, "Most of Her Majesty's colonels have red noses."

At anchor, a little outside the lighthouse on the Kingston pier, lay the *Swift*, a ten-gun brig, "very trim, bright, and rakish." At the dock, well-manned boats of the *Dragon*, a war steamer, waited.

The prisoners were hurried on board the *Dragon*, and in two or three minutes were carried to the *Swift*. By half past three the trip to the bottom of the world had begun.

"You will not be harshly treated," the captain told the exiles. "You may smoke, but you must obey the regulations and only two of you will be allowed on deck at one time. You may not speak to any member of the ship's crew — only to the surgeon and to me."

As the *Swift* passed from St. George's Channel into the Atlantic, Meagher saw a few more Irish landmarks and then Ireland passed from his gaze forever. The rest of the voyage of 111 days proved uneventful except for a twenty-four hour sojourn at Simon's Bay, Cape of Good Hope. The southern tip of Tasmania, known as Van Dieman's Land until 1853, came into view on October 28, and the next day the *Swift* anchored in the harbor of Hobart, then called Hobart Town.

While the captain and most of the crew were ashore, the prisoners, under charge of a marine guard, watched boats putting off from the shore to circle the *Swift*. One of these, it turned out, had an Irishwoman aboard. Her husband had been in some earlier Irish trouble and been transported. She had followed with their children. Now she greeted the new exiles. Her warmth and her brogue cheered them, even though she told O'Brien, "It's a quare home your coming to."

That evening in the captain's cabin the assistant comptroller of convicts for Van Dieman's Land interviewed the prisoners.

"I have been instructed to grant you tickets of leave," he informed them.

Meagher asked, "And what, sir, may a ticket of leave be?"

"A ticket of leave is a permit granting you freedom to move about in restricted portions of the island. Not everywhere, you understand, only in certain places and districts."

"That's fine," said O'Donohue, thinking that perhaps he might move far enough away from the assistant comptroller of convicts not to see him or Van Dieman's Land again.

"But there are certain conditions attached to giving these privileges," the assistant comptroller continued. "The first is that the captain here will testify that your conduct during the voyage was satisfactory — "

"I'll testify to that," said the captain emphatically.

" — and the second is that you will pledge yourself as men of honor not to use the freedom you get under these tickets of leave to escape."

This was quite another matter. But with a sea voyage of fifteen thousand miles more or less between them and Ireland, and a year of confinement behind them, the exiles were not inclined to split hairs. And so Meagher, McManus, and O'Donohue gave their pledges. O'Brien, who was with them, refused.

Then they learned that there was still another regulation. They were to be separated. They could not live in the same town or district.

Meagher was assigned to Campbelltown on the east-central portion of the island; O'Donohue was to be sent to Hobart Town on the southeast coast; and

McManus was to have headquarters at New Norfolk,
north of Hobart Town. Because O'Brien refused to
give his pledge, he was assigned to Maua Island, on
the east coast off Oyster Bay. The loneliness of the
exiles grew less painful as two distinguished visitors,
Father Hall, vicar-general of the Diocese of Tasmania,
and Father Dunn, a missionary to the island, came
aboard to welcome them.

In a few days the exiles parted to settle in their
respective districts. Meagher made his home in Ross,
within his district, but seven miles from Campbelltown. Here he struck up a warm friendship with an
Irish gentleman, and the companionship they formed
prevented him from living like a hermit. Meagher
devoted his mornings and evenings to reading and
study. In the afternoons he strolled along the Maquarie
River, or sailed, or rode horseback through the brush
in pursuit of the kangaroo. Meagher's prosperous
father apparently provided money for his son's needs.

The districts in which the prisoners were confined
were areas of some size. Meagher's, for instance, was
from thirty to thirty-five miles long and ten to fifteen
miles wide. He had not been in Ross long, however,
before he and Martin and Doherty, earlier exiles, discovered a method of meeting together without violating regulations.

The districts touched at a common point. This, to
quote Meagher, was a "small, cozy, smoky bit of a
log hut, inhabited by a solitary gentleman named
Cooper." The hut stood on the shore of a "noble" lake,
twenty miles from Ross, in a chain of mountains
called the "Western Tier." The hut was "high enough

to admit one in an upright position of any reasonable
extension of legs, spine, hat, and shirt collar. The
furniture consists of something to sleep on — I don't
know what to call it; a table, very weak in the ex-
tremities; two stools, a block for splitting chips upon;
a shelf, three feet in length, and furnished with a
couple of pewter plates, a gunpowder flask full of
pepper, three breakfast cups, a carving knife, a breakfast knife, forks to match, a tract upon foreign mis-
sions, and two columns of a *Sunday Observer*, bearing
a remote date."

To reach this meeting place, Doherty had to ride
twenty miles and Martin twenty-five. Usually the
friends met on Monday, scheduling their trips so that
at about 11 they rode out of the brush at the same
time. They dined together; and while one prepared
the meal, the others rambled along the shores of the
lake, singing old songs and making plans for the
future.

In the southern hemisphere these were warm,
glorious summer days. In defiance of regulations and
in spite of a sixty-mile ride each way, McManus sometimes came up from his district to spend a few happy
hours with his friends. They cheered one day when
John Mitchel joined the Monday gathering at the
lake. Mitchel had arrived in Van Dieman's Land in
April, 1850, so broken in health that the government
permitted him to live with Martin in the Bothwell
district.

In spite of these weekly get-togethers, time hung
heavy on the hands of these vigorous young men. It
did not make them any less restless when the au-

thorities subjected them to minor punishments. When Meagher violated the regulations by visiting Mitchel, who was sick, he was kept a prisoner for some time in his own house. McManus took matters into his own hands, and having forfeited his ticket of leave, escaped by boarding a steamer bound for San Francisco. His friends paid his passage.

On February 22, 1851, Meagher was married to a Miss Bennett, the daughter of a farmer living near New Bedford. For his bride, who is described as a "most beautiful young lady," he built a pretty cottage on the shore of Lake Sorell and there lived happily. Most men would have settled down. But not Meagher. His proud spirit resented the restrictions which the ticket of leave placed upon his movements and activities. He wanted to escape to a land "in which a useful and honorable career will be open to me."

In April, 1851, he was asked to renew his ticket of leave pledge. He did so, but by December 27 he had made up his mind to escape. In order not to violate his pledge, on January 3, 1852, he wrote to the police magistrate of the district of Campbelltown that at noon the next day he would surrender his ticket of leave, so that after that time he would no longer be bound by his parole. He warned the magistrate that if he tried to arrest him before that time, he would interpret such action as freeing him from his parole obligations.

At 11 o'clock the same morning, Meagher's letter was delivered to the police magistrate. Although certain that an attempt would be made to arrest him, Meagher remained in his home at Lake Sorell until

7 that evening. He had made thorough preparations to escape.

A few minutes after 7, four of his friends galloped up and told him excitedly: "The police are coming to arrest you."

With his friends as company, Meagher rode into the bush to a point about three hundred yards from his cottage and there waited. Finally his servant came out with the news: the police had come and were sitting in Meagher's kitchen.

"It's time to go, boys," Meagher said.

The five mounted their horses immediately, and rode quietly toward the house. When they had come to within about a hundred yards of it, Meagher held up his hand.

"I ride forward alone," he told them. They did not dismount. The servant walked next to Meagher.

The stable stood within pistol shot of the kitchen door. When he reached it, Meagher told the servant, "Tell the police I am waiting for them."

The servant disappeared into the kitchen. Two or three minutes later, the police rushed out. The moment they appeared, Meagher rose in the stirrups.

"I am the prisoner you came to arrest," he shouted. "I defy you to catch me."

At the same time, his friends gave three "loud and hearty cheers," and all five galloped off into the woods in the direction of the northern coast of Tasmania. It was Saturday evening.

Apparently the police were either too astonished or too unprepared to pursue effectively. Meagher's account does not suggest that the escape was difficult.

The arrangements seem to have been most thorough. For the time being Mrs. Meagher remained in Tasmania.

On the way to the coast Meagher and his companions stopped at a house to change horses, and one of the men had time to write out an account of the escape for the leading newspaper of Van Dieman's Land. Meagher's other three friends signed the account. They were concerned that Meagher should not be accused of violating his pledged word and they did not want to be accused of assisting him to do so.

On Monday afternoon the six men rode down to the seashore and there, by prearrangement, a boat was waiting. It was manned by two poor fishermen who had been hired by Meagher's friends to sail him to one of the small, uninhabited islands which dot the Bass Strait between Tasmania and Australia. Although the island selected lay only four miles from the nearest point in Tasmania, it was a forty-mile trip for Meagher and the fishermen from their point of departure. The sea was wild that day, the boat small, and the passage "most perilous." The island proved small, desolate, and wind-swept.

According to plans, the ship that would pick Meagher up the next morning would carry him to Pernambuco, now called "Recife," a seaport lying on the eastern extremity of Brazil. From there he would take another ship to the United States.

The morning after they reached the island the three men waited impatiently on the shore for distant sails to appear. The day dragged; the ship did not arrive. They rose the next day, to wait with less hope. And the next. By evening of the third day the provisions ran out, and the boatmen sailed away to the mainland for a fresh supply. They did not return.

After that, for seven endless, lonely days, with hope diminishing each hour, Meagher waited and wandered alone on the barren crag, looking toward the sea, hearing the pounding of the surf and the lonely cry of the gulls. His food during this week consisted of shellfish and birds' eggs.

Finally, ten days after he first set foot on the island, when it happened that he was not watching, Meagher was startled by the firing of a gun. A ship had crawled in close, and, as it shortened sail, the captain clung to the rigging and waved a white handkerchief. This apparently was the signal agreed upon and Meagher stood out in full view. The ship, the *Elizabeth Thompson*, rounded a point in the island, dropped anchors, sent out a boat to pick up the passenger, and returned to her course. She was eastbound for London by way of Brazil.

At Pernambuco, Meagher left her to take passage to the United States on the American brig *Alcorn*. He reached New York on March 26, 1852.

He was three months short of being thirty years of age. Men the world over knew his name and fame. He had created thunder on two continents. Now he would make thunder on a third.

Chapter V

TEMPEST RENDS THE REPUBLIC

AMERICA has always thrown open her arms to liberty-loving exiles from other lands. The story of the Young Ireland movement was well known and the names of the leaders were household words. It was to be expected that Meagher's arrival would prove an occasion of national rejoicing, much like the arrival several years before of the great Hungarian patriot, Louis Kossuth.

Moreover, pestilence, the potato famine, and English misrule had swollen the small stream of Irish immigration to the United States into a flood, and large numbers of Irish were to be found in many places, particularly in the big cities of the North.

Now newspapers and magazines talked about Meagher; delegations waited on him to tender him public dinners and receptions, or to invite him to speak. Mayors, governors, city councils, state legislatures, almost as one voice, welcomed him.

His greatest satisfaction came on meeting some of the old Confederates of the Young Ireland conspiracy who had escaped before him. On the day that Meagher reached New York, one of them, Michael Phelan, handed Meagher a pocketbook.

"You'll need something to live on," Phelan said. "I presume that you'll be receiving funds from Ireland. This should help until they come."

Meagher looked at Phelan sharply. "Tell me the truth, my friend. Is this all the money you have?"

It was all the money that Phelan had. Meagher was deeply touched by Phelan's generosity. Meagher, however, did not seem to lack cash. His prosperous father apparently had defrayed all the costs of his escape.

Meagher spent his first days in America at the home of his friend, Devin Reilly, in Brooklyn. There, Michael Cavanaugh visited him. Cavanaugh had known Meagher well in Ireland, and remembered him as "a handsome, well-built young fellow, with genuine Celtic features, laughing blue eyes, and dark brown, rather curly hair." Now he found him looking "more manly and resolute." Meagher seemed more robust. His face was tanned by his outdoor life in Tasmania, and by his four months' voyage. Still, "his carriage

was as graceful, and his step as light, firm, and resolute," and the tone of his voice as youthful and light-
hearted as Cavanaugh remembered them in Dublin.
Meagher still dressed with the same fastidiousness:
dark frock coat, light vest, and gray trousers. Only in
New York he was wearing a wide-brimmed straw hat.

Although Meagher gratefully and politely discouraged the efforts of people the country over to show
him public honors by arranging banquets and other
testimonials, he felt he should accept the invitation to
review the annual parade of the New York National
Guard on the Fourth of July following his arrival.

A reviewing stand, decorated with flags and bun-
ting, had been constructed on Broadway. Tens of
thousands of people lined the curbs and sidewalks.
Little boys shot off firecrackers, while little girls held
their ears.

The parade brought together miles of policemen,
volunteer fire brigades pulling their apparatus, fra-
ternal societies, marching clubs, turnvereins, fife and
drum corps, military bands, garrisons of regulars from
the New York harbor forts, and the New York National
Guard.

Meagher stood at attention in the reviewing stand
as the colors of the well-drilled ranks of the Guard
marched by.

Many Irish had enlisted in the Guard, and some of
its companies, horse and foot, had been recruited
wholly among the New York Irish. As these groups
of marchers passed before the reviewing stand, to the
tune of "St. Patrick's Day," Meagher exclaimed,
"Would to God we had these men upon the old sod."

That evening Meagher sat at the speakers' table at the banquet given by the officers of the Guard. General Sanford rose and offered a toast: "To the health of Thomas Francis Meagher — a traitor to England, but the young and devoted champion of Irish liberty!"

Meagher did not then know that the thrill which passed through him at the sight of his countrymen marching under the Stars and Stripes would set off a chain of circumstances that nine years later, at the outbreak of the Civil War, would draw him powerfully to enlist in the service of his adopted country.

Now his old friends of revolutionary days in Ireland, who in three years' time had organized these fine military groups among the newly arrived Irish, asked themselves: "If Meagher was so thrilled by the Fourth of July parade, why shouldn't we call a general muster of all these Irish militia and have him speak to them?"

So it happened that, to honor Meagher, on July 27, 1852, Battery Park at the lower end of Manhattan Island was crowded with soldiers and with tens of thousands of Irish.

After reviewing the troops, Meagher, with some of his friends, entered Castle Garden, once a fort, then an immense hall, and now a monument and a shell, to be welcomed by the Guard and to respond to the welcome.

Colonel Michael Doheny made the address to the "grand assemblage."

"You see here many of your countrymen in arms. In a grateful and proudly confident spirit they rally around the starry flag of liberty, determined to justify the confidence of their adopted land.

"Those who accept the arms of liberty assume the responsibility of defending her.

"To your comrades in captivity we beg you to communicate what you see and hear today. Tell them that as long as their mighty hearts are not broken there is room for hope. Tell them that their honorable deliverance is the first thought of their armed countrymen in these free states."

In his response Meagher dwelt on the advantages of freedom in the United States.

"Here, the poorest trader, the poorest mechanic is cheered in his drudgery by the proud thought that he, as well as the wealthiest, is an active and essential component of the State — that by his vote he affects the direction of her government, and by his arms, and the habits they impose, co-operates in her defense."

While loving Ireland as most exiles love the country of their birth and children the land where their fathers are buried, and while hating her oppressors and waiting for the chance to strike at them, the Irish did not wait long to declare their first allegiance. They had come to America to escape the Old World. America gave them shelter and the rights of free men. They would become American citizens.

On August 9, 1852, less than three months after his arrival in New York, Meagher appeared unattended before the clerk of the Superior Court of the United States. He listened while the oath he was to take was read to him.

"Thomas Francis Meagher has personally appeared before the subscriber, the Clerk of the Superior Court of the United States for said District of New York, and made oath that he was born in Ireland, and that it is BONA-FIDE his INTENTION to become a CITIZEN OF THE UNITED STATES, and to renounce forever all allegiance and fidelity to any foreign Prince, Potentate, State or sovereignty whatever, and particularly to Victoria, Queen of England, of whom he is a subject."

At this point Meagher interrupted: "I do not consider myself Queen Victoria's subject. I have been declared an outlaw by the British government."

After some explanation, Meagher took the oath. He treasured the copy of his Declaration of Intention to become an American citizen. It was the first official document he received from the government of the United States. Many others would follow.

Meanwhile, Mrs. Meagher was on her way to join her husband. Arrangements had been made that, if he succeeded in escaping, she should follow him to New York with his father, whom she would first join in Ireland.

From the time of his arrival, Meagher had been looking about for some way to earn a living.

"You should become a lecturer," his friends told him again and again. "There are hundreds of thousands of people who want to hear you."

"Cities throughout America have invited you to visit them."

"You could serve the cause of Ireland and freedom by lecturing."

Meagher finally yielded to the persuasions of his friends and decided to give lectures in the many cities that had invited him to be their guest. While waiting for his tour to begin, he prepared a volume of his Irish speeches for publication. Within a year the book ran through several editions.

In November, 1852, Meagher began his tour. Audiences everywhere filled halls to overflowing to hear him.

Meagher's tour through the South brought him into the Washington depot. "Are you going to accept the invitation of the President to show you the hospitality of the White House?" he was asked.

"I could not arrange my schedule to permit me to do so," he answered. "It is a matter which I cannot control, but deeply regret."

Meagher's reception in the South was a continuous ovation. Nowhere else in America did he feel so much at home. He loved the Southerners for their warmth of heart and made hosts of friends among them. For this reason his decision to stand by the Union when war came was most painful and difficult for him.

In January, 1853, Meagher returned to New York at the completion of his first long lecture tour.

His wife and father arrived late that spring, and during the summer and autumn they vacationed together in New York State, visiting Niagara Falls, Lake George, and the beautiful Catskill Mountains. Meagher had agreed to make a lecture tour through California that winter, and when Mrs. Meagher grew unwell, he thought it better that she should return to Ireland with his father, to rejoin him in New York in the spring. He never saw her again. She died of a fever in Waterford the following May, at the age of twenty-two, after giving birth to a boy.

Meagher meanwhile had delayed his departure for California. Good news had come from Van Dieman's Land. The newspapers carried exciting headlines: "John Mitchel Has Escaped!"

When Mitchel arrived in New York, as always he was bubbling over with a great scheme. He would publish a weekly paper to be called *The Citizen*. His purpose would be to tell people everywhere that Irishmen in Ireland were not so abject as to be "loyal" to the sovereign of Great Britain, nor were Irishmen in America resigned to accepting the defeat which had driven them from their homeland. Meagher agreed to become Mitchel's associate in the venture. Meagher's gift of writing attracted him to journalism. Overnight *The Citizen* became an outstanding success.

The hopes of Irishmen at home and all over the world rose at the beginning of 1855. England was deeply involved in the Crimean War, and to use them against the Russians, she withdrew troops from her garrisons in Ireland.

"This is a good chance for Ireland to get her liberties," some of the Irish Nationalists in New York agreed.

"Sure it is. While the English are fighting the Russians on a peninsula in the Black Sea would be a good time to jump on England's back and free Ireland."

To further this plan, certain Irishmen in New York organized the secret Emmet Monument Association. Robert Emmet, one of the greatest of Irish patriots, had been hanged in 1803 for armed insurrection. The Association named for him enlisted armed and disciplined men in military organizations which were pledged to the cause of Ireland's freedom.

The scheme went so far that its leaders contacted Russian representatives in Washington and New York.

For a time it seemed that Russia might attempt to arm and outfit an expedition to fight England in Ireland. Whether the United States would have permitted such a violation of neutrality is another matter. In any event, the sudden ending of the Crimean War put an equally sudden ending to such schemes.

Although Meagher did not become an enrolled member of the Emmet Monument Association, he knew of its existence, sympathized with it, and by his speeches in every quarter of the Union, he roused Irish blood to fighting pitch. By his fiery words as well as by his heroism, he drove despair from Irish hearts. The Monument Association later changed its name to the Fenian Brotherhood — "The Fenians."

Although events were moving fast in the spring of 1856, and the nation was giving evidence of dividing itself — the newly formed Republican party put forth its first presidential candidate in the fall election of that year — Meagher's life seemed to be settling down. In May, he married Miss Elizabeth Townsend of New York, and shortly afterward founded a newspaper of his own, the *Irish News*.

The venture proved successful and Meagher should have been content, but he grew restless. After leading a revolution, and traveling constantly, activity which confined him to a desk and office soon seemed tame.

Nevertheless, he waited two years before he turned over the *Irish News* to his assistant and made a tour of Central America for *Harper's Magazine*. The tour resulted in a series of travel articles for the magazine and a new set of subjects for lectures for Meagher. The articles and the lectures both proved so successful that when *Harper's Magazine* asked Meagher to return to Central America in the summer of 1860, he readily consented. While he was gone from New York, an event took place that did much to change the rest of his life.

It was reasonable that to the Irish who had suffered starvation, eviction, injustice, persecution, exile, and other great wrongs, Queen Victoria, as the nominal head of the English government, should be hated for what she stood for. This hate became apparent to all the world when the Prince of Wales — "his mother's son," as the Irish put it — on a tour of America, visited New York in the fall of 1860. The Prince was a well-mannered, good-natured young man, as the Queen was a good wife, mother, person, and ruler, one of the greatest in England's history, even though during her long reign some of its worst disasters befell Ireland.

Motivated partly by genuine hospitality, partly by curiosity, and partly by a kind of toadying to titles, America turned out to greet the handsome visitor who came, as Meagher later said sarcastically, "to place a feather in the cap of Liberty."

A parade was arranged for the Prince, and the New York National Guard were ordered to march. "Lawfully as a citizen, courageously as a soldier, indignantly as an Irishman" — the words are Meagher's — Colo-

nel Michael Corcoran, who was a general in the
Fenian Brotherhood as well as a colonel in the National Guard, "refused to parade his stalwart regiment [the 69th New York, the "Irish regiment"] in
honor of the beardless youth, who, succeeding to the
spoils of the Tudors and Stuarts, was destined one day
to wield the scepter that had been the scourge of
Ireland."

Corcoran's refusal brought down much abuse on his
head, and for weeks the newspapers of the world discussed it. But it also brought a salvo of applause from
true lovers of liberty everywhere, and particularly
from the Irish.

Recruits swelled the ranks of the marching Fenians,
and the quality of men they enlisted improved. The
Irish felt an upsurge of pride in their history and
blood.

As the St. Patrick's Day parade swung down Broadway on March 17, 1861, Meagher stood with other
notables on the reviewing stand. City, state, and national officials were there; representatives of the clergy
and hierarchy; high officers of the Army and the Navy;
important men in all walks of the nation's life.

The precision of the marching of the Fenian Brotherhood brought an exclamation of admiring surprise
from everybody on the stand. So did the superb
drilling of Corcoran's 69th Regiment of the New York
National Guard, and of Irish companies in other
parading regiments.

As Meagher watched transfixed, pride rose in him
for the old race; and an idea, long put aside, lay hold
of him: liberty could be better bought by the sword

than by the pen. He would forsake the rostrum for the drill field. That morning the Irish ladies of New York presented the 1st Regiment of the Phoenix Brigade with a silk Irish flag. At the ceremony Meagher made up his mind. That night, impulsively, he joined the Fenians.

For months, ever since the election of Lincoln during the preceding November, a tempest had been tearing the American republic apart. One by one, the Cotton States had left the Union to form the Confederacy.

It became more and more apparent, to quote Lincoln, that the house divided could not stand. The country was filled with the tinder of war and only a spark was needed to set the fire raging. It was not hard to guess what would happen, though the time and place were less definite.

Twenty-six days after Meagher joined the Fenians, the South fired on the Stars and Stripes over Fort Sumter in Charlestown Harbor, and there was war.

Within hours the kettledrum of the recruiting sergeant began to thrash and rattle on the streets of New York. Among the first to rally to the colors everywhere were the Irish.

The outbreak of war posed difficult problems for Meagher. While he kept more or less independent of politics, on the day he became a citizen of the United States he declared that he believed in the principals of the Democratic party. From time to time he spoke at Democratic meetings.

When his father-in-law called the Southerners "rebels," Meagher disagreed. "You cannot call eight million white freemen 'rebels,' sir. You can, if you will, call them 'revolutionaries.' "

In the months after South Carolina left the Union, but before Sumter, Meagher was outspoken in his views. "In the quarrel between the North and South," he told his friends, "my sympathies are entirely with the South."

This was the attitude taken by many Irishmen. They felt that the Southerners had the same right to assert their independence from the North as Irishmen had to assert Ireland's independence from England.

In a moment, Sumter changed all this.

When he read how the flag had been fired upon, Meagher exclaimed: "I feel like one carried away by a torrent. The whole cry is — 'The Flag! The Flag!' " And then he added — "Damn them that did not let the flag alone!"

Knowing Meagher's feeling of great friendliness for the South, his friends asked him if this outburst meant that he might join the Northern army.

"Yes, I do not see what better course I could take," Meagher answered immediately. "Duty and patriotism alike prompt me to it. The republic that is the mainstay of human freedom the world over is threatened with disruption. Above all, it is the duty of us Irish citizens who aspire to establish a similar form of government in our native land."

"But a great many may be killed," his friends objected. "Dead men will be of no service to Ireland."

Meagher had an answer: "If only one in ten of us comes back when this war is over, the military experience gained by that *one* will be of more service in a fight for Ireland's freedom than would that of the entire ten as they are now."

Even before Sumter, in the first week of April, 1861, Meagher proposed to organize a second regiment of the Phoenix Brigade of the Fenian Brotherhood.

A company of "Phoenix Zouaves," unattached to any regiment, had already been organized. When this company learned of Meagher's proposal, it sought and received permission from General Michael Corcoran, commander of the military portion of the Fenian Brotherhood, to put itself under Meagher's command. Before it had a chance to meet and extend the invitation to Meagher, the war broke out.

Chapter VI

LEADEN RAIN AND IRON HAIL

THE Phoenix Zouaves considered Meagher their captain, even though the Fenian Brotherhood had not commissioned him and he therefore had not formally accepted the rank.

When war broke out, whole companies of the Fenian Brotherhood joined the New York National Guard, bringing many of their officers with them. In this way Meagher became a member of the 69th New York Regiment, with the rank of captain.

Over a half million people lined New York streets

on April 23, 1861, when the 69th — the famous "Fighting Irish" — marched down Broadway on its way to Virginia. A little before 3 o'clock, the head of the procession swung into the densely crowded street. A great cheer rose and rolled along with the marchers for miles.

"Who are those handsome men riding at the head of the regiment?" everyone asked.

"That lean man in the middle is Colonel Michael Corcoran, the commander. The man to his left is Judge Charles P. Daly. And the man to the Colonel's right — "

"Don't tell me. That must be the great Meagher himself."

The regiment carried two flags. The first was the Stars and Stripes; the second, the flag of Ireland.

As the lines passed by, bareheaded Irishmen were heard to say, "Remember your country and keep up its credit, boys." And, "What harm if it was to Ireland they were going?"

The regiment embarked at Pier Number Four, North River. Arriving at Annapolis, they found orders waiting for them. They were to proceed to Georgetown, outside of Washington, and occupy the Heights and Georgetown College — now Georgetown University. The 69th found the Jesuits friendly and the quarters ample. The classrooms were big enough for a company to drill in and the dining hall could seat five hundred at one time. From two stately pines the Irish regiment made a ninety-foot pole from which to fly the Stars and Stripes.

Meagher's company did not leave with the remainder of the regiment. Its ranks were still not filled. Meagher's first task was to recruit, not to fight.

A month after the rest of the 69th had left New York, Meagher was in Washington. His company and 200 other recruits had taken a train to Baltimore and from there marched to the Capital.

Starlight glittered and the corner street lamps shed dim, yellow light on the Zouave uniforms of the Irish soldiers.

"Look trim there, boys," Meagher commanded briskly. "This may not be Broadway, but it's Pennsylvania Avenue, where the President rides in his carriage on inauguration day."

Meagher himself looked like a captain of a pasha's guard as he sat comfortably on a handsome horse. He was wearing his Zouave uniform: baggy trousers, tight black coat, and a hat looped up at the side.

As the regiment swung into the broad street, the band struck up "The Wearing of the Green":

> "O Paddy dear, and did you hear
>   The news that's going 'round:
>   The shamrock is forbid by law
>   To grow on Irish ground;
>   St. Patrick's day no more to keep,
>   His color can't be seen,
>   For there's a bloody law against
>   The wearing of the green."

Yes, there were bloody laws against the Irish in Ireland, but not here in America. So must many a man in the smartly marching lines have thought that night as with baggy trousers lightly slapping, and the dust of Washington swirling under their feet, the Zouaves paraded past the Capitol with its half-finished dome, past the sprawling city, and out through the open country to Georgetown.

On the day that Meagher reported to Colonel Corcoran, the 69th received orders to cross the Potomac into Virginia. On the Virginia side of the river, and back from it about half a mile, a low range of hills known as the Arlington Heights extends for about five miles. In the middle of the range, and directly across from Washington, stood Arlington, the home of Robert E. Lee. Two bridges, about equal distance from the Lee-Custis mansion, provided crossings into Washington. The upstream bridge, known as the Aqueduct Bridge, led directly into Georgetown.

To hold Washington, it was necessary for the Federal army to seize and hold Arlington Heights. To accomplish this purpose, they sent a force of about 8000 men across the Potomac as far south as Alexandria. The 69th was assigned the task of holding the hill next to the Aqueduct Bridge. As each command reached its post, it immediately commenced to erect a large earthwork.

When they passed out the shovels and the officers told the men to begin to dig, it is not difficult to imagine the comments.

"I joined the army to fight, not to dig holes."

"I just got the calluses off my hands, and here they give me a shovel."

"We left Ireland because we were tired of digging potatoes."

"Faith, it's not potatoes we're digging here. And

if you don't dig, it's likely the rebels will give you something bigger and harder than potatoes."

Someone has said that good soldiers always grumble. The men of the 69th worked with a will and in a week built a fortification 650 feet long and 450 feet wide.

Lincoln and several members of his Cabinet came to watch the men toil and gave much encouragement by their compliments. Although Colonel Corcoran named the works "Fort Seward" in honor of Lincoln's Secretary of State, the War Department changed the name to "Fort Corcoran," and so it remained. When the flag was first raised over the fort, Meagher made a brief speech.

For about six weeks after the completion of the fort, the 69th occupied it, drilling by day and guarding the bridge and the Heights by night. Ten West Point cadets were temporarily assigned to the regiment as drillmasters.

"Mere boys to show us how to march, and to hold our guns in fancy ways, and how to 'whip up the hand smartly in salute,'" some two-fisted, tough survivors of famine, cholera, the rising of '48, and English jails must have thought. But discipline improved.

Toward the beginning of July, Archbishop Hughes of New York and Bishop Timon of Buffalo visited the regiment, and when Father Mooney, the chaplain, returned to New York, his place was taken by the Jesuit Father O'Reilly. In the absence of Major James Bagley, Captain Meagher acted as major.

News from the South meanwhile excited much speculation.

"I see here that Jeff Davis has moved his capital from Montgomery, Alabama, to Richmond. I wonder what that means for us?"

"I'll tell you what it means: the rebs will try to take our capital, while we try to take theirs. It means that we'll meet them halfway between Richmond and Washington in a big fight — "

"A big fight? There won't be a big fight. They'll run when they see us. That's why President Lincoln asked us to enlist for only three months."

"There are Irishmen among the rebs, too. I wonder if they're talking that big."

"Well, if they're going to have us fight, they'd better hurry. Our time in the army is running out."

The top men in Washington knew *that*, and, moreover, many people in the North thought that the war could be ended by one big battle, with an easy victory for the North, of course. And so northern newspapers began to clamor, "On to Richmond."

Responding to these pressures, General Irwin McDowell, who commanded the Union army around Washington, with headquarters in Arlington, moved with 50,000 troops in mid-July against the Confederates. About 40,000 southern troops, commanded by General Beauregard, lay at Manassas Junction, along Bull Run Creek, about 40 miles from Washington. This was considered the strongest military position between the two capitals. Another Confederate force, led by General Joseph E. Johnston, was stationed at Winchester to prevent Union General McClellan, who was in western Virginia, from joining McDowell.

McDowell, in turn, had stationed General Patterson

at Martinsburg to keep General Johnston from rein-
forcing Beauregard. Spies in Washington told the
Confederates of the Union plans almost as soon as
they were made.

On the evening of July 15, as the Stars and Stripes
flapped from the 90-foot pole, Colonel Corcoran called
the 69th to attention on the parade ground. Meagher
stood behind him.

"Something's up," was the whisper in the ranks.
"The Old Man's got big news."

The news turned out to be an order for the 69th
to advance into Virginia the next day.

The Union army set out in five columns. McDowell
hoped to gain the rear of both Beauregard and Johnston, seize the railroad, and, by getting between them
and Richmond, take possession of the Confederate
capital.

The advance was made without much resistance.
As one column, which included the 69th and was commanded by William T. Sherman, entered the village
of Fairfax Court House, the enemy retreated from the
other end of town.

"Where are the Confederates?" the men of the 69th
wondered. Up to this point they had met no opposi-
tion, although they were hot and perspiring from the
hard work which the withdrawing enemy had forced
upon them. Every half mile or so the road was blocked
with enormous, fallen trees, which had been dragged
into heaps by the withdrawing Confederates. The
pursuers had to hew a way through the obstructions
with axes.

The Union army was in high spirits. "We'll march

right into Richmond and no one will stop us," they boasted.

Such talk did not take into consideration the untried bravery of the Union forces nor the excellence of the Confederate generals. Beauregard was merely drawing McDowell into a tight spot.

McDowell now saw that his plan to get in the rear of Beauregard could not be carried out, and so he massed 25,000 of his forces around Centreville. At noon on July 18, the Stars and Stripes were flying over the village as the 69th made awnings by stretching blankets over frames of muskets and fence rails, and sat down beneath them to enjoy lunch.

They were confident and happy. The enemy seemed bent on retreating. Here was the Union army, within four miles of Manassas. Although at intervals of ten to twenty minutes, in the hazy woods below them, the booming of a gun told that McDowell had caught up with Beauregard, and that the Confederates were making a stand, they remained very cool.

An aide rode up to Colonel Corcoran at 4 that afternoon. Sherman had received orders from McDowell. His brigade was to move to the front to relieve regiments that had been under fire for four hours.

The 69th took the lead, and away they swung behind the two flags, in the hot, brilliant sunshine and amid choking clouds of dust. In an hour they halted at the brow of a hill descending into a little meadow. Here regiment after regiment had stood in a storm of shot and shell from Confederate batteries and muskets. The withdrawing regiments filed past them, carrying their wounded.

"Lie down and hold your fire," the 69th was ordered. The men could not fail to note with admiration the coolness of their officers.

"Look at Colonel Corcoran there, standing like a statue in the middle of the line. And Captain Hagerty to the left. And Captain Meagher and the rest."

Toward evening, General McDowell rode up, surveyed the enemy's position, and, closing his field telescope, turned to Sherman and Corcoran.

"It's too strong to be attacked successfully," he said. "Return the 69th to Centreville."

There McDowell held his army for two days while he sought information and rations. The delay proved a great advantage to the Confederates, who used it to make movements unknown to McDowell. When McDowell had reached Farfax Court House, Davis ordered Johnston to join forces at Manassas with the army of the Shenandoah. Instead of fighting Patterson, Johnson eluded him, and with 6000 infantry arrived at Manassas at noon on the twentieth and, being senior to Beauregard, took command. The rest of his force followed more slowly. Now the Confederates not only outnumbered McDowell by 4000, but were sheltered by strong defenses.

This delay, unfortunate though it was for the Union army, brought a great benefit to the 69th in the person of a dust-covered visitor. It was Father Scully, chaplain of the Boston Irish Regiment.

"You must have had a long ride," Colonel Corcoran said as he greeted Father Scully.

"Thirty-five miles, Colonel."

"And to what do we owe the honor of a visit?"

Father Scully's eyes twinkled: "I heard that there was some fighting, and more coming up, and I rode out from Washington to satisfy my curiosity."

"Good for your curiosity," observed Father O'Reilly. "And now that you have satisfied it, you can help me hear confessions. The Johnny Rebs yonder seem to be spoiling to turn some of these Irish soldiers into saints, and my part of the business is too heavy for the moment for one man."

Meagher wrote, "Few of the 69th failed to confess and ask forgiveness on that day. Everyone, officers and privates, prepared for death. It was in truth an affecting sight — that of strong, stalwart, rugged men — all upon their knees, all with heads uncovered, all with clasped hands in prayer and eyes cast down, approaching one by one the good dear priest, who, seated at the foot of an old bare tree, against which some of our boys had spread for him an awning of green branches, heard the confessions of the poor fellows, and bid them to be at ease and fearless. It was no less impressive than that of Father O'Reilly's passing along our line, as we knelt within range of the enemies' batteries on one knee, with bayonets fixed, expecting every instant to be swept upon, and the final benediction was imparted."

McDowell saw the need for immediate attack. With the three months' enlistments expiring, his army threatened to melt away. Accordingly, on July 21, under a bright moon at 2 a.m., the army began its advance from Centreville to Manassas. It marched south in three columns.

McDowell's plan was to deceive the Confederates

by feigning an attack against the Stone Bridge across Bull Run. Meanwhile, two of the columns would make the real assault against the Confederate left.

The battle was opened when a Union shell burst over the heads of the troops of Confederate Colonel Evans, who guarded the Stone Bridge. Beauregard reinforced Evans, thinking that the feint was the real attack. Johnston ordered an attack by his right, and Ewell advanced and was thrown back.

Johnston and Beauregard were anxiously watching the battle from a hill, when far to the north they saw a dust cloud moving toward them. They were not sure what it meant.

"Does it mean," Johnston asked Beauregard, "that General Patterson has discovered that I have slipped by him, and have joined forces with you, and he is now hurrying to join his force with General McDowell's?"

The answer was long in coming.

The Confederates by now guessed McDowell's plan, and, as heavy blue columns marched through the forest, were able to predict where the real Union attack would strike. Nevertheless, when the assault came, the Confederates were pushed back and compelled to rush in reserves. Then McDowell sent in reinforcements. Soon only a small stream separated the fighting armies. Among the regiments hurried into the Union line was the 69th. Assistance was badly needed because the men at the front were nearly exhausted. They had been on their feet since midnight.

When another New York regiment made a furious

charge and forced back the Confederates, General Thomas Jackson arrived with reinforcements.

"They are beating us back," Confederate General Bee told Jackson.

"Well sir," Jackson replied, "we will give them the bayonet."

"Form, form in line," Bee ordered the fugitives. "There stands Jackson like a stone wall." The Confederates rallied and ever since the name has been "Stonewall" Jackson.

It was now noon, and Johnston and Beauregard, watching the battle from a distance of four miles, sent heavy reinforcements in waves.

Turning over to Beauregard the command of the field, Johnston rode to a high place from which he could look down not only on the battle itself, but on the country toward Manassas. While the column of dust had moved closer, he still did not know whether it rose from Federals or Confederates. He looked for help from that direction. Unless aid arrived, he had little chance of success.

While he waited, he sent in more reinforcements, so that by 2 o'clock, when the battle was resumed, the Confederates had 10,000 men and 22 guns on the plateau held by their left.

The Union army too was struggling for position, and by 1 o'clock the right had seized the Warrentown Turnpike. Now they needed only to push the Confederates from the plateau, and they would defeat them, seize Richmond, and end the war.

The battle see-sawed on the plateau, with heavy losses on both sides. The 69th was in the thickest of the fight. Three times it charged through the deadly showers of the Confederate artillery, and three times it was driven back. Meagher wrote after the battle that whenever the Federal troops had a fair chance, they whipped the Confederates and that the Union infantry was more than a match for the Confederate. But, "we yielded to their batteries."

During the long fight, Meagher served as major of the regiment and special aide to Colonel Corcoran. After the battle, when the correspondent of the *London Times,* who did not like Irish patriots, suggested that Meagher had not done his full duty, 23 officers of the 69th signed a statement saying that "no officer or soldier could have borne himself more gallantly, nor with more perfect coolness and intrepidity," than Meagher did all through the "labors and terrors of that battle."

It seemed to these officers that Meagher was everywhere. "His exertions were incessant throughout the day — now delivering orders — another time encouraging the men — hastening up stragglers on the march — keeping the men compact and silent in the ranks — doing everything an officer could do to excite the ardor and insure the efficiency of the regiment. Riding cooly and deliberately along the line, in front of the enemy's batteries, from which a tempest of ball and shell swept the field, while in the act of delivering the Colonel's order to prepare to charge, Captain Meagher's horse was torn to pieces by a cannon shot. From that time on, he took his place with a company of Zouaves on foot, advanced upon the enemy's batteries, cheered and inspired the men as they rushed upon the works, and in the face of the deadliest fire, with his head uncovered, stood his ground, waved his sword, rallied the 69th in the name of Ireland, when the regiment was twice repulsed, and was among the last, if he himself was not the very last, to leave the fatal spot where so many of his honest-hearted countrymen were slain."

When Johnston heard of the slaughter on the plateau, he grew discouraged. "Oh for four regiments," he said. It was now 3 o'clock, and four hours before he had ordered three fresh regiments to the line. But they had not arrived, and the Union army apparently had victory in its grasp.

Almost as he spoke, Johnston saw a cloud of dust arise in the direction of the Manassas Gap Railway. It could mean only one thing — reinforcements!

General Smith had arrived with 4000 men from Johnston's Shenandoah force, and was rushing to join Beauregard on the battlefield. A great cheer greeted Smith's troops. They increased by almost half the strength of the Confederates on the plateau.

Quickly the tired, outnumbered Union forces were overwhelmed, and regiment after regiment broke and began to retreat down the turnpike. Confusion turned to panic, and panic became rout, so that at 4 o'clock McDowell's army was a mob streaming toward Washington. With it were Congressmen, ladies, and other civilians who had come out in carriages from Washington to picnic and see the fun. The fleeing army left behind 3000 killed, wounded, or captured. The Confederate loss was less, only 2000. Had the Confederates followed up their victory, they might have had little trouble in seizing Washington.

When the last attack of the 69th failed, and the retreat from the Confederate guns began, Corcoran ordered the survivors of the 69th to form a square and withdraw to the ford at which it had crossed Bull Run. When the regiment reached the ford the narrowness of the wooded path leading down the bluffs to the water compelled it to re-form into a column. Sherman was in the middle of the square.

"Move on as fast as you can," he shouted. "The enemy cavalry are coming!"

Most of the 69th crossed Bull Run safely and again attempted to form a square. Sherman's order, however, caused confusion — someone said it was a "license to run," and while Corcoran was trying to restore order at the rear of the regiment, he was surrounded and captured by the pursuing Confederate cavalry.

Meagher himself escaped capture only by a lucky chance. During the last attack by the 69th, Meagher was following the regiment through the smoke and uproar as it fiercely fought its way out, when he was knocked head over heels and left senseless.

Fortunately for Meagher, after the third repulse of the 69th, the 2nd U. S. Cavalry was ordered to move toward the road leading to Centreville, to hurry on the stragglers and to cover the retreat. As the order was given, Private Joseph B. McCoy, who had left St. Francis Xavier College to join the regulars, saw Meagher lying on the ground, within a couple of hundred yards of the Confederate batteries. McCoy was faint with hunger. It was now 5 in the afternoon, and except for a cracker and a little water he had eaten nothing since 2 in the morning. His horse had fared little better.

In spite of his weakness and dizziness, McCoy broke from his companions, galloped past Meagher, grasped him by his collar, jerked him across the saddle, and carried him away from the guns. Although Meagher regained consciousness as McCoy galloped off, his weakness was so great that he could only clutch at his rescuer, and he was afraid of slipping to the ground. McCoy, on his part, expected every moment to be pulled from the saddle by Meagher's weight.

But they reached safety, and when Meagher slid to the ground, McCoy said, "Captain, if I were a volunteer, I'd give you the horse, but being a regular, I can't do it."

When Meagher rose he found himself in a group of Fire Zouaves — former members of a city volunteer fire brigade who still wore fireman's uniforms — and men from the 8th and 71st Regiments. All were walking toward Centreville.

Meagher hitched a ride from an artillery wagon which overtook the group. As the jolting vehicle began to cross the bridge over the creek which runs between Centreville and Manassas, two or three hundred members of the Confederate Black Horse Cavalry broke screaming from the woods. In the scramble that followed, one of the wagon horses was shot, the wagon was tipped over, and Meagher was thrown into the water.

Up to this point, Meagher saw no panic among the Union troops around him. They were walking as unconcernedly as if strolling along an autumn road.

Then suddenly the Union wagon train dashed madly upon them: commissariat wagons, ambulances, hospital carts, artillery forges. As drivers screamed and beat horses and mules, the wagons ran into one another and tipped, harness and traces became entangled, horses fell, and the writhing animals blocked the crossings.

Only the prompt action of a pair of guns, which dashed up and drove off the Black Horse Cavalry with a shower of canister, prevented terrible havoc.

Meagher dragged himself out of the river, rejoined the throng of retreating soldiers, and soon reached the field where he had encamped the three preceding nights. There he found Dr. Smith and about fifty soldiers of the 69th.

"Another three or four hundred of the boys are on the road to Fairfax," he was told. "They are bound for Fort Corcoran. Colonel Sherman told us that Colonel Corcoran was wounded and had passed ahead in an ambulance." This was wrong information. Corcoran had been captured.

"Take my horse," Dr. Smith insisted when Meagher expressed a wish to catch up with the body of the regiment.

A mile or so beyond Centreville, Meagher overtook the main body of the 69th. It was marching in good order toward Georgetown.

"Here's Captain Meagher."

"Glad to see you escaped, Captain Meagher."

The surviving officers were unanimous. Meagher was the ranking officer present. He should take command. The regiment halted for a few minutes while the matter was settled.

Meagher rode forward, "All right boys. You gave a good account of yourself. Keep ranks closed. Forward march!" And while the 69th made an otherwise uninterrupted march of thirty miles, late afternoon turned to twilight, twilight grayed into dusk, the stars appeared, and the night grew cool, quiet, and empty. In spite of their last-minute success, the Confederates made a poor pursuit. They seemed almost as much surprised in victory as the Federals were in defeat.

Chapter VII

THE HEAVENS THEMSELVES
ARE OPENED

THE 69th waited at ease in the parade ground at Fort
Corcoran. Meagher stood before them smiling, with
a War Department order in his hand.

"I have news for you, men. It will probably make
many of you unhappy." Meagher paused. "We are
ordered to break camp today and return to New York.
The War Department recognizes that your three
months' enlistment has expired."

A great cheer went up.

That evening, while another regiment waited to move into their place, with many upward glances at the Stars and Stripes on the 90-foot flag pole, the 69th crossed the Potomac into Washington and bivouacked on the White House grounds.

Unless the soldiers of 1861 — most of them young — were different from their counterparts today, as is not likely, there was a great deal of craning of necks.

"Is this where Old Abe and Mrs. Lincoln and the children live?"

"I wonder if Old Abe is home tonight, or is spending the evening with the boys."

"Maybe he wouldn't like to have me sleeping on his lawn if he knew that I voted for Steve Douglas."

The bugle blew early next morning and the regiment again paraded down Pennsylvania Avenue. Its battle flags had Virginia dust on them now, and a few scars. At noon it crowded onto the train to Baltimore.

Baltimore was considered a Southern city. After Sumter, the first Union regiments to cross through it enroute to Washington had been mobbed.

To reach the New York train it was necessary to leave one station and march to another. The 69th fell in outside the depot.

"Look your best," Meagher ordered. "There'll be some here who aren't our friends."

But if Southerners were present, they were silent. Not so the Irish, who were numerous in Baltimore and who waited along the route to cheer.

This Baltimore reception was only a foretaste of a greater demonstration when the 69th marched up Broadway. The people of New York had read the accounts of its bravery at Bull Run and they turned out to see the heroes.

Captain James Kelly, as senior line officer, led the triumphal march. At his side rode Meagher. First reports had it that Meagher had been killed at Bull Run and his appearance was greeted with wild cheering. The regiment was mustered out of the service of the United States on August 3, 1861.

Shortly after, Meagher returned to Washington to visit some of the wounded of the 69th who had been left behind in hospitals. While he was there, the War Department offered him a captaincy in the regulars.

"Of course you will accept the commission, Captain Meagher. It is a high honor."

"I know that," Meagher said. "It is so high an honor that I feel I have not earned it. Others deserve it more than I do, and I would not keep the honor from one of them by taking it."

"What are you going to do?"

"I am going to ask the War Department to offer it to some more experienced officer of the 69th."

As a result of this generous refusal by Meagher, the commission was offered to Captain James Kelly, who accepted it.

Meagher's bravery received wide recognition and the distinguished Missouri statesman, Frank P. Blair, called Meagher to the attention of Major General John C. Fremont.

Fremont — the "Pathfinder" — was a national hero. He had explored the West, helped seize California during the Mexican War, become the Republican candidate for the presidency in 1856, and was now commanding the second largest army of the North, with headquarters in St. Louis.

"Will you accept the position of aide-de-camp on my staff, with the rank of colonel?" Fremont telegraphed.

Meagher showed the telegram to his friends.

"I would like to accept the position," he told his friends.

"Then why don't you do so?"

"Not when plans are under way to reorganize the 69th for three years' service as United States Volunteers. My place is with the men whom I have led in battle."

"And you also refused to take the command of the second regiment of volunteers being organized among the Irish of New York?"

Meagher smiled. "I belong to the 69th," he said quietly, but firmly.

When talk commenced of recruiting an Irish brigade for the Union army, with the 69th as the first regiment, it was agreed that the command should be offered to the most distinguished American military leader of Irish birth — General James Shields.

Born in Ireland, Shields had come to America as a young man and made his way to Illinois. There he became a lawyer, a member of the legislature, and state treasurer.

Shields had challenged Lincoln to a duel, and Lincoln accepted, but backed down, and the two became friends. Shields was one of the heroes of the Mexican War. In the Civil War he became the only general to beat Stonewall Jackson, and he lived after the war to gain the distinction of being the only American to serve as United States senator from three different states.

The officers of the old 69th chose Meagher to seek the approval of the War Department for the formation of the Irish brigade. Plans became more ambitious. The brigade would consist of five regiments. Three of them, of which the 69th was the first, would be recruited in New York. A fourth regiment would be organized in Pennsylvania, and a fifth in Massachusetts. There were a great many Irishmen in both states. In addition to these infantry regiments, the brigade would have its complement of cavalry and artillery.

On August 30, 1861, the War Department answered "Colonel" Meagher. Provided he could have it ready for marching in 60 days, the 69th would be accepted for three years' service, or for the duration of the war. Meagher was also authorized to deal with the colonels of the four other Irish regiments to be organized.

The recruiting, organizing, and equipping of the Irish brigade took longer than anticipated, and it was three months before it was ready for marching orders. It finally consisted of three regiments of infantry and two batteries of artillery, all New York troops. The governors of Pennsylvania and Massachusetts refused to allow their regiments to join it.

The ladies of New York had prepared two flags for each of the regiments: the Stars and Stripes and the green flag of Ireland. The latter was emblazoned with gold emblems: a sunburst, harp, and shamrock wreath. A scroll bore in Gaelic a line from the ancient Irish poet Oisin: "Never retreat from the clash of spears."

Prior to its departure for Washington, on November 18, 1861, the 69th received its flags in front of the residence of Archbishop Hughes on Madison Street. The Archbishop himself was to have made the presentation. But Lincoln had sent him to Europe as a personal representative to try to keep Catholic countries from favoring the Confederacy, and so the vicar-general of the archdiocese, Dr. Starrs, presided at the ceremony. The 69th was first to leave; the 4th and 5th Regiments were still recruiting.

Meagher now served as colonel of the 10th Artillery and as acting chief of the Irish Brigade. When it seemed that a war with England was likely over the "Trent Affair," in which an American naval captain stopped an English ship at sea and removed two Confederate envoys from it, Meagher wrote: "War with England is imminent. *The Irish Brigade will be the first to meet the music.* The 4th and 5th Regiments must hold themselves in readiness for marching orders. *Ireland's* day has come!"

The 4th and 5th Regiments finally left New York on December 16, and two days later joined the 69th at "Camp California" on the Fairfax Turnpike near Alexandria, Virginia.

Meanwhile no news came from Shields. In those days neither telegraph nor railroad connected the Pacific coast with the rest of the country, and news traveled slowly. Shields had left California before the invitation to take command of the Irish Brigade reached him. He was in Mexico. His health was poor, and the rumor spread that he would not accept appointment as brigadier general of volunteers, a rank below that which he held in the Mexican War.

"It sounds reasonable," the officers of the Irish Brigade said to one another. And they agreed that "Meagher has really done the work of organizing the Brigade and therefore deserves to command it." Before their regiments left New York, the officers of the 4th and 5th held a meeting, and on December 19 a committee of officers of all three regiments waited on President Lincoln to urge Meagher's appointment. The next day Lincoln sent Meagher's name to the Senate for confirmation as brigadier general of volunteers.

On January 5, 1862, before the Senate approved Lincoln's nomination, Shields reached Washington. Although he had received the War Department's offer in Mexico, and had returned to California and there taken the first ship to New York in expectation of commanding the Irish Brigade, Shields now used his powerful influence with the Senate to secure the appointment for Meagher. He called on his friend Lincoln. Shields had already been commissioned a brigadier general, at Meagher's request, Lincoln told him. Now Shields told Meagher's friends, "I know that Meagher possesses all the qualities necessary to make a good general, and only wants the practice and opportunity to develop them."

The Senate confirmed Meagher's appointment on February 5, 1862, and the War Department assigned him to command the Irish Brigade. Later Meagher and the officers of the Brigade tried unsuccessfully to persuade the War Department to organize all Irish regiments in the army into a division, and to commission Shields a major general and give him command of it.

On receiving his commission Meagher rode out to Camp California where the Irish Brigade, 3000 strong, waited in winter quarters for the opening of the spring fighting. Shields accompanied him.

After Bull Run, during the months in which Meagher was organizing the Irish Brigade, the morale of the North was low. Sensible people began to realize, as not all of them had realized before, that the war would not be won in a single battle, or in a month, or by a handful of volunteers.

As a result, recruits by the tens of thousands swelled the ranks of the small, bedraggled Union army. Drillmasters took over. Great camps sprang up around Washington and war became big business. A dashing young general, George B. McClellan, succeeded Mc-Dowell in command of the Army of the Potomac, and then Scott in command of all Union armies. The victories in western Virginia, for which McClellan received the credit and which had pushed him into supreme command, had actually been won by his lieutenant, General William S. Rosecrans, one of the ablest fighters, North or South, of the Civil War.

McClellan's army numbered over 150,000 men. He had two hundred pieces of artillery. Again the cries of "on to Richmond" began to be heard in the North, but, except for minor engagements, McClellan refused to move and spent eight months organizing and disciplining his army. Toward the close of this period of inactivity the Irish Brigade joined it.

Finally Lincoln's patience was exhausted and he ordered McClellan to advance.

On March 15, 1862, Meagher read McClellan's orders telling that the "time for action had arrived." The Irish Brigade greeted the news with the "wildest enthusiasm." The next day, with the 69th in the van, the Brigade set off for Fairfax Court House, and on the morning of St. Patrick's Day it crossed Bull Run. Many who had fought there remembered the place. It remained in the vicinity for a week, on guard, watching the distant Confederates. Someone would say, "Would it were upon the plains or mountains of Ireland we were marching, and that those were English campfires yonder."

Orders came on the twenty-fifth that General Sumner's Corps, to which the Irish Brigade was attached, should return. McClellan's plans had now matured.

Instead of moving directly south and overland against Johnston, who still guarded Richmond, McClellan judged it best to carry his army on ships to Fortress Monroe, at the tip of the peninsula formed by the James and York Rivers, and to march it northwest up the peninsula toward Richmond. From this plan the campaign takes its name: the Peninsular Campaign.

It was a good plan, badly carried out from the beginning. The first upset came when Lincoln held back for the defense of Washington thousands of troops that McClellan counted upon and needed. Then the Union army wasted almost a month besieging Yorktown, where in the Revolutionary War Cornwallis surrendered to Washington. The Irish Brigade missed this siege. It had embarked at Alexandria, near Washington for Fortress Monroe, and from there it marched toward Yorktown. Before it arrived there, the Confederates had withdrawn and were making a stand at Williamsburg; and needing reinforcements, McClellan ordered the Brigade to hurry forward.

It set out at nightfall in a heavy rain. Ahead, the road stretched like a flooding marsh, with mud so deep and sticky that the wheels of the artillery, which went first, constantly got stuck. Behind the artillery the infantry halted, impatiently. When it became clear by 2 a.m. that further marching in the sodden night was useless, the Brigade bivouacked in a woods. Having learned next morning that the Confederates had again withdrawn, the Brigade returned to Yorktown. Up to this point the campaign had been slow, but seemed successful. Johnston now stood with Richmond directly behind him.

From Yorktown the Irish Brigade advanced westward toward Richmond to a new camp on the east bank of the Chickahominy River, which flows into the James, and for two weeks waited without a fight. To break the monotony, the men organized a steeple chase.

On the evening of Saturday, May 31, just as the horses finished running, the thunder of artillery and the rattle of musketry broke out in the woods along the Chickahominy. Meagher guessed what was happening. Johnston had caught McClellan with his army divided by the flooding Chickahominy River, and at

Seven Pines was attacking the exposed corps. He hoped to crush it before it could be rescued.

Although the bridge was gone, during the night engineers threw up a makeshift, and in the darkness the greater part of Sumner's Corps, including the Irish Brigade, crossed and hurried toward the front.

When the Irish Brigade woke from its bivouac next morning, it was astonished to find the enemy within pistol shot. The Confederates were equally astonished. Two miles to the rear of the Brigade, ran the flooding Chickahominy. And four miles before it lay Richmond.

One of Meagher's engineers, who had been a sailor — an immense, shaggy, iron-built fellow, with a tanned skin and a tempestuous eye, agile and daring as a tiger — darted up a towering pine close to the railroad, and caught a glimpse of the dome of the confederate capitol flashing through the smoke of the city. He saw church spires and the shining fragments of bridges over the James River. "I can see Richmond," he shouted.

Richardson's two brigades — the Irish Brigade was one of them — threatened not only Richmond but the Confederate army. Two hundred paces beyond Richardson's lines and almost parallel to them lay the tracks of the important Pamunkey and Richmond Railroad. Behind the railroad stretched the Confederate lines. The enemy hoped to drive the Union army away from the railroad, and into the flooding Chickahominy River. The day before it had almost succeeded in so doing. But the exposed Union wing had desperately persisted, and finally counterattacked.

Now the counterattack was resumed and under a hurricane of bullets the 69th swept up to the railroad and deployed along the tracks. The rest of the Brigade followed them.

"That day," said Meagher, "the chivalry of Virginia met its match in the chivalry of Tipperary." Soon the wounded began to be carried back to a field hospital, a little barn, "abounding in fleas and mice, and super-abundantly carpeted with damp hay." There was to be seen the "good, kind, gentle priest of the old and eternal Faith calming the fevered brain with words which at such moment express the divinest melody and transform the cloud of death into a home of splendor."

When the battle seemed in the balance, old General Sumner rode up to the Brigade, took off his hat, exposing his gray hair, and told Meagher that the Irish were his last hope. "If you fail me all is lost." Then he pointed to his shoulder straps. "But I'll bet my stars on you. Now I want to see how Irishmen fight. And when you run, I'll run."

The men cheered heartily and, with Meagher leading them, advanced into the woods as though they meant to stay. Soon the crash of musketry told that they had met the enemy, and by noon their cheers announced that the enemy were falling back. Meagher believed that had the Union army pushed them hard at this time the Confederates would have retreated through Richmond and beyond.

Shortly after this an officer dashed back from the battle line with Meagher's report. Meagher's aide wore a long, grizzled mustache that coiled up under his eyes. General Sumner listened. "That was a gallant fight the Irish Brigade made, Captain Gosson."

Gosson modestly raised his cap at the compliment. "Egad," he said in a thick Irish brogue, "we gave them a healthy dash." From that day on, Sumner swore by the Irish Brigade.

History calls this great fight, in which the Irish Brigade bore a gallant part, the Battle of Fair Oaks or Seven Pines. Losses on each side were about 7000 men. When it was over, the Federals held the field, while the Confederates had a new commander. General Johnston was severely wounded and General Robert E. Lee succeeded him.

For almost a month after Fair Oaks, the Union Army lay on the banks of the Chickahominy, threatening Richmond but accomplishing little. Although rumors told the North each day that on the morrow a great battle would be fought, the next day came and went without fighting.

During this time Meagher and the Irish Brigade held a portion of McClellan's front line. Once, when the stint lasted without relief for eight continuous days and nights, the men could hardly keep awake in the ranks. Occasionally the enemy in force attacked the Union pickets.

Lee broke the deadlock and put McClellan on the defensive by quietly withdrawing Jackson from the Shenandoah Valley, and sending him on June 26, 1862, to fall on McClellan's great supply base at the White House. At the same time he ordered Longstreet to cross the Chickahominy and fall on the Union right. That day, near Mechanicsville, a great battle was fought in which the Confederates lost between 3000 and 4000 men, while the Federals lost only about 400.

Although this victory put Richmond at McClellan's mercy, he concluded, contrariwise, that he lacked sufficient forces to fight Lee to his front and to guard his supply line to his rear. If his army were based in the James instead of the Pamunkey, he could supply it directly by water. And so he ordered a retreat across the peninsula to the James. Lee now attempted to overtake and destroy McClellan; and for a week, in a series of tremendous fights called the Seven Days' Battles, McClellan resisted Lee's efforts.

In the first of these great battles, at Gaine's Mill, the Confederates attacked McClellan's rear guard commanded by General Porter, who had arranged his troops in an arc between Cold Harbor and the Chickahominy. Under pressure of heavy attack Porter called on McClellan, who was across the river, for reinforcements. First McClellan sent a division over, and then, fearing that Porter might still be getting the worst of it, he hurried the brigades of Richardson and Meagher to his help.

Reaching Porter in the woods near nightfall, they found him badly overmatched. His column was out-flanked and falling back in confusion to the hill in the rear of its position, with the Confederates on its heels.

The two brigades rushed forward and saved the day. A company of the 69th New York, by a determined bayonet charge, checked the stream of fugitives pouring toward the bridge over the Chickahominy. The enemy recognized the singing cheers of the Irish Brigade. They had heard them before, at Bull

Run and at Fair Oaks. Porter's men rallied behind their rescuers and, turning on the Confederates, checked their advance.

During the night, while the Irish Brigade covered the approaches to the bridge, Porter's Corps crossed to rejoin the main body of McClellan's army. After that, and before the baffled enemy could muster courage to attempt to follow, Meagher destroyed the bridge.

In the other terrible battles that followed, at Savage Station, the Peach Orchard, White Oak Swamp, and Malvern Hill, the Irish Brigade gave a good account of itself.

At Malvern Hill, in the dusk of evening, the 88th New York, advancing in heavy woods, suddenly came upon the "Louisiana Tigers," a battalion from New Orleans, well known for its fighting qualities. At close quarters the Tigers used pistols and knives instead of guns. Lacking these weapons and having no time to fix bayonets, the Irish used their muskets for clubs, and their fists as well. In the midst of the roughhouse a giant member of the 88th saw a mounted Confederate officer cheering on the Tigers. Leaping toward him, the Irishman seized him with his great hand and pulled him off his horse. "Come along, you spalpeen," he roared, as he dragged him to the Union lines.

The next morning an officer of the 88th visited General Sumner with a requisition for muskets. On the retreat across the peninsula some Union soldiers had carelessly lost their guns or thrown them away. Whenever Sumner heard about such occurrences, he grew very angry. Now he told the officer requesting muskets, "You shall not have them, sir. I'll take all arms from you and make your men dig trenches. They are not fit to carry arms."

"You're mistaken, General," said the officer. "My men did not lose them or throw them away."

"Where are they then?"

"Outside, sir. I thought you'd be wanting to see them."

Sumner went out, and his jaw dropped when he saw a pile of muskets, with bent barrels, smashed stocks, twisted bayonets.

"What happened?" he asked quietly.

The officer grinned. "It's the 88th, sir. Last night we got into a scrimmage with the Louisiana Tigers, and when the bloody villains drew knives, our boys mostly forgot their bayonets, and went to work in a style they're accustomed to. They licked them well, too, sir."

Sumner's face lost its hard look. He let it be known after that — and the Irish Brigade loved him for saying it, and repeated it among themselves — that he thought he could whip the whole of Lee's army with the Irish Brigade and Pettel's Battery.

Chapter VIII

LIGHTNING STRIKES IN THE WILDERNESS

VOLUNTEER replacements for the Union army were no longer easy to secure. The time had passed when a drummer thrashing a drum or an orator making a patriotic speech could bring crowds of boys and men to sign their names on muster rolls. The long lists of dead and wounded posted at home after each battle made it clear that war was no picnic. And the men who returned maimed or with cheeks hollowed with illness, and told about those who would never return, made even restless young men hesitate. Newspapers

113

began to carry advertisements for artificial arms and legs and cripples became a common sight.

"It's bad enough to serve under an ordinary general," people began to whisper among the New York Irish. "But under Meagher — ?"

"He's got a great love of his own glory. He takes chances with his soldiers that a more careful general would not take. He's as reckless as he's brave."

Although all agreed that Meagher took the same or greater chances than his men, and led wherever he asked them to go, the charge was hard to answer. Certainly it was safer to follow a more timid general.

But Meagher's friends rose to his defense both with words and with pocketbooks. By personal subscriptions the members of the New York Corn Exchange raised a fund to pay a bounty of $10 apiece to the first 300 recruits enlisting in the Irish Brigade. In 1862, $10 bought many times more than it does now, and this sum was in addition to city, state, and federal bounties.

Austin Kelly & Company, a Canal Street firm, added a further offer of $10 for the first fifty recruits and continuous employment during the war to their wives and daughters. Private citizens made similar offers. And yet recruiting lagged.

Meanwhile, the army of the Potomac suffered further humiliation. McClellan's peninsular scheme had ended in retreat, and Lincoln's confidence in him was badly shaken.

Searching for a new general, Lincoln chose John Pope, whose success at Island No. 10 in the Mississippi was judged the most brilliant in the war. Pope was placed in command of the army before Washington. Gradually much of the army on the James was brought back to reinforce him.

Full of bluster, Pope met Lee at Manassas on August 29 and 30, 1862. Again Lee and Jackson proved too much, and a disheartened Pope led the defeated army back to Washington.

Because the Irish Brigade was not among the troops transferred to Washington to reinforce Pope, it saw no part of the Battle of Second Bull Run, or Manassas. When Meagher rejoined the Brigade at Harrison's Landing, however, he had every reason to believe that it would see battle in the near future.

Wise men in the Union army predicted: "Now is the time for Lee to attack, before the new men reach us." They were referring to the fact that on July 1, before Pope's defeat, Lincoln had called for 300,000 more volunteers. Alarmed, the Confederate government ordered Lee to attempt to capture Washington before these new troops could be put into the field.

Knowing that he could not carry the great forts screening Washington from the front, Lee resolved to circle the city and thrust at its rear. Accordingly he crossed the Potomac, in September, 1862, and from Frederick issued a proclamation calling upon the people of Maryland to rise. This invasion caused Lincoln to remove Pope from command. Pope had lost the army's confidence. The army cheered McClellan's return. When McClellan learned that Lee was in Maryland, he advanced toward Frederick with about 90,000 men.

The Irish Brigade was jubilant when Meagher announced orders to march double-quick down the peninsula to Fortress Monroe.

"We're going to stop Lee," they shouted.

Ships waited at Fortress Monroe, and from there the Brigade steamed up Chesapeake Bay into the Potomac, and up the Potomac to Washington. It was "hurry, hurry" all the way to Washington; and "hurry, hurry" from Washington to catch up with McClellan in Maryland.

At Frederick, McClellan discovered Lee's plan. Lee proposed to take possession of Harper's Ferry, open communication with Richmond through the Shenandoah Valley, draw McClellan far into Pennsylvania, turn suddenly, and defeat him, and then fall on Washington.

McClellan followed Lee from Frederick in two columns. On September 14, McClellan's right struck Lee at Turner's Gap, and his left, moving nearer Harper's Ferry and trying to get between Lee and the Union garrison there, fought its way through Crampton's Gap. Unfortunately for McClellan, the commander at Harper's Ferry surrendered just when rescue appeared certain.

By September 16, the Confederate army was posted along the heights on the west side of Antietam Creek near Sharpsburg, Maryland.

That night, Hooker, with part of his corps, crossed the Creek at the extreme right of the Confederate line, and the next morning, with about 17,000 men, he assaulted the Confederate left and center in a fight that lasted late in the afternoon.

At Antietam Meagher and the Irish Brigade again

distinguished themselves for bravery. Sumner's Corps was advanced to reinforce and replace Hooker's, which had opened the attack. At 9:30 on September 17, Richardson's division of Sumner's Corps, including the Irish Brigade, crossed Antietam Creek to its assigned position, with Meagher on the right. In the distance, artillery thundered, musketry rattled, and the air was blue with sheets of smoke and dust. Men looked to their guns and fixed their bayonets.

Ahead the ground was very rough. It was intersected with ravines and dotted with hills covered with growing corn. Stone walls enclosed the tilled fields. Behind these walls the enemy could advance unseen to fire upon exposed Union positions.

As Richardson's three brigades approached the battle lines, Confederate gunners opened fire. Within sight of the battle the Irish Brigade received orders to halt at the edge of the woods. Canister and solid shot tore through the trees overhead, bringing down showers of twigs and leaves and whole limbs, but even though bursting shells made the waiting men wince, the fragments struck no one. Up to this point the irregularities of the ground sheltered the men, and the inability of the Confederate gunners to find accurate range made them secure.

"Couldn't hit the broad side of a barn," was a reasonable comment.

Although the wait seemed endless, it could not have lasted half an hour. Then orders came. The Irish Brigade was to cross the field before it and, moving directly to the front, enter the battle line.

Meagher rode to the head of the column. Drums

began to roll. The Stars and Stripes and the green of
Old Ireland folded and flapped in the breeze. At the
command to march, the men cheered.

When the cheering Brigade climbed the crest of the
ledge in front of it, the hard-pressed men in the fighting line turned their heads for a second, saw Meagher
and the green flags, and recognized their rescuers.
Then, they too, broke out into cheers. As they filed
out of position Meagher's men filed into their places.

The correspondent of the London *Times* was on the
field. He was a sharp-tongued Englishman, with no
love for Meagher and the Irish. Nevertheless, he
grudgingly paid the highest tribute to the conspicuous
bravery of both that day.

Two lines of Confederates lay in front of Meagher.
Both were very strong. In the first line the enemy
were concealed by a rise in the ground, so that only
their heads were exposed.

Union bugles screamed "Charge!" and drums began to roll. With Meagher in the lead, the Brigade
hurled itself forward. As it advanced, its continuous
front was momentarily broken, when the center ran
into a rail fence which, only a few minutes before,
had sheltered Confederates.

"Tear the fence down!" Meagher shouted. "Get it
out of our way!"

Although the fire was hot, and men fell constantly,
the fence was quickly demolished and the charging
line made whole. The Confederates scurried, and with
a wild cheer the Brigade took the crest.

It now faced even greater odds. Ahead stretched the
road to Sharpsburg, which at this point is several feet

lower than the shoulder to each side. The Confederates had converted this sunken road into a rifle pit, and lay in great strength behind it. Partially concealed to the rear of the road, a supporting force of Confederates waited.

Naturally the road was the most hotly contested point in the line. The London *Times* correspondent wrote: "The musketry fighting at this point was the severest and most deadly ever witnessed before — so acknowledged by veterans in the service. Men in large numbers fell every minute, and those who were eyewitnesses of the struggle did not think it possible for a single man to escape. The Brigade suffered terribly."

Here for four hours the battle raged. When Meagher ordered the final charge against this position, the whole Brigade gave a cheer that could be heard for a mile along the Union line.

Leading his men on horseback, Meagher proved a prominent target. His horse was shot from under him and a bullet passed through his clothes.

The 63rd, "always conspicuous for deeds of daring in battle" — the compliment was given by the London *Times* correspondent — outshone itself. Sixteen times its colors were shot down, and each time another man sprang forward, raised the fallen banner, and bore it in the van.

Deeds of heroism were numerous. Seizing the flag, a sixteen-year-old youth, John Hartigan of Company H, rushed out far in advance of his comrades and waved it defiantly in the face of the enemy.

One soldier noted that the "enemy seem to have a special spite against the green flag," and five color bearers were shot down in a short time. When the fifth fell, even the Irish themselves hesitated until "Big Gleason," captain of the 63rd, who measured six feet seven, sprang forward and picked it up.

A few minutes later, when a bullet struck and shattered the staff, Gleason wrapped the flag around his body, fastened his sword belt over it, and so carried it through the fight.

When the Brigade finally seized the sunken road, it found it filled with Confederate corpses. A Union battery had fired into it the long direction. The scene was "one of the most ghastly of the war." The Brigade used this trench as a breastwork and held it until the fight was over. Not a single Union defender there was captured, and not a single one strayed.

Nevertheless the loss of life was extremely heavy. The 69th brought 317 men into the Battle of Antietam. Of these, 196 or 61 per cent were killed or wounded. The record of the 63rd almost matched this. Of its 341 men present, 202 or 59 per cent were killed or wounded. The entire brigade suffered 540 casualties.

McClellan reported that at Antietam the "Irish Brigade sustained its well-earned reputation. After suffering terribly in officers and men, and strewing the ground with their enemies as they drove them back, their ammunition nearly expended and their commander, General Meagher, disabled by the fall of his horse, shot from under him, this brigade was ordered to give place to General Caldwell's brigade, which advanced a short distance to its rear. The lines were passed by the Irish Brigade, breaking by company to the rear, and General Caldwell's, by company to the front, as steadily as on drill."

While the Union right was thus engaged, the left would have crushed Longstreet had not Lee rushed in reinforcements.

The Battle of Antietam lasted fourteen hours, and when darkness ended it the advantage was McClellan's. He had begun the fight with 80,000 men to Lee's 60,000, and 14,000 more were marching to reinforce him next morning. Lee lacked reinforcements and his supplies were low.

McClellan should have crushed Lee. Instead, Lee crossed the Potomac to strong positions south of the Rappahannock while McClellan followed slowly.

Accordingly, he was removed from command, and his friend, General Ambrose Burnside, was put in his place. Burnside, like McClellan a good man and in some respects a good general, protested that he did not want the appointment. But he took it nonetheless.

If McClellan proved too cautious, Burnside proved too rash. And his rashness spelled catastrophe for his army and the Irish Brigade.

While commanders were being changed, the Brigade itself was reorganized. At Antietam a fourth regiment, the 29th Massachusetts, had been temporarily attached to it. While this regiment contained many Irishmen, it could scarcely be called an Irish regiment. To replace it, the 116th Pennsylvania volunteers — a freshly recruited Irish regiment was ordered to the Brigade, and on November 23, the 28th Massachusetts, which had been specially raised for the

Brigade, but assigned elsewhere, was finally transferred to it. Again the Irish Brigade was Irish in all its parts.

The losses it had suffered were apparent. The five regiments together could muster only about 1300 men.

Meagher shook his head in disapproval. "That's about as many men in the five regiments as the 69th alone mustered when it set out from Fort Corcoran to Bull Run. The Irish Brigade is scarcely bigger than a good-sized regiment."

Meanwhile the tattered banners of the three New York regiments had been sent home to be preserved as souvenirs. Generous people had offered to provide new flags, and Meagher arranged a program for their acceptance. Invitations were sent to most of the prominent generals in the army and the quartermaster traveled to Washington to secure food and drink for a banquet. But delivery of the flags proved slow.

On taking command, instead of laying plans for destroying Lee's army, Burnside began to look for ways of reaching Richmond. His forces numbered about 120,000 men. He hurried to post these north of the Rappahannock River at or near Fredericksburg, Maryland. From this point he thought he could march on Richmond. Fredericksburg is about fifty-five miles north of Richmond, and sixty miles south of Washington.

To block him, Lee gathered about 85,000 men south of the river, and 300 cannons, and destroyed the bridges for miles.

Fredericksburg was easy to defend and difficult to attack. The Rappahannock there is bordered on both sides by hills. On the northern bank these lie parallel to the river and close to it. On the southern, they form a semicircle six miles long and two to three miles wide. Within this plain lay Fredericksburg, a town of 5000. Behind the town the hills are high and treeless, but eastward of it, lower and densely wooded. Wooded spurs extend at right angles into the plain.

"It's strong — very strong," Meagher must have thought as he listened to spies and scouts, or looked through his telescope at Lee's army which guarded the hills and spurs for a distance of six miles. Longstreet's Corps held the line near Fredericksburg, with its right on Marye's Hill. On the crest was posted the famous Washington artillery.

A road skirted Marye's Hill, and fronting it, so that it could not be seen across the plain, stretched a massive stone wall. To convert this wall into a breastwork a brigade of infantry had dug entrenchments behind it so deep as to conceal riflemen. Longstreet's position was an impregnable fortress.

A frontal attack exposed the attacking column not only to the fire of the riflemen behind the wall, but to the flanking fire from a row of pits dug behind a rail fence, which ran diagonally from the wall toward the town. Meanwhile the massed artillery in the heights could reach every square foot of the ground over which an attack must move. On the day before the battle Longstreet's chief of artillery, Colonel Alexander, crowed, "We will comb the field as with a fine comb. A chicken could not live there when we open fire."

The plain itself, between the town and the wall,

was intersected midway by a millrace or canal. Two roads leading at right angles from the river and through the town crossed the canal, again at right angles, on plank bridges.

Burnside had been preparing for several days to cross his army. On December 9, 1862, he called together his commanders and told them that Marye's Hill held the key to Lee's position, and that he would assault it.

Along the Chickahominy, on the early morning of December 11, mists rose thinly as the Union engineers pushed pontoons into the water and laid planks across them to make five bridges over which Burnside hoped to cross.

On the south bank, Confederate sharpshooters waited in buildings along the stream. A rifle barked and a man carrying a plank splashed into the river. Finally 170 Union guns spoke, and as the nearest buildings crumbled, the bridge builders resumed their work.

Early on the twelfth the Union army began an unopposed crossing, and by evening the greater portion of it occupied Fredericksburg. The thirteenth was quiet except for an artillery duel; and many soldiers in both armies thought that Burnside would withdraw rather than attack Lee's stronghold. Unfortunately they were wrong, and the next morning the Union army lined up in attacking columns in the streets of Fredericksburg.

Meagher limped out that morning to face the Brigade. He was suffering from a boil on the knee. The surgeon had lanced it prematurely and his leg was stiff. It was very painful for him either to walk or ride. Nevertheless he led the Brigade throughout the day.

"We'll miss our old flags," a New York officer said. "It won't seem right to go into battle without them."

Boxwood hedges stood at the front of some of the yards in Fredericksburg. Plucking a sprig from one of these, Meagher stuck the evergreen into the front of his cap, so that it stood up like a cockade.

"I told the men that they should carry the colors of the fatherland into battle," Meagher explained to the officers. "Now follow my example, and tell your men to do the same."

The Brigade broke ranks to make an assault on the hedges of Fredericksburg. They were back into column, each man identified by the color of the land of his birth, just as General Hancock and his staff rode up before the attack.

Meagher and Hancock passed slowly in front of the Brigade. To each of the four regiments Meagher spoke briefly. Then the men marched bravely out upon the field of death.

The key attack on Lee was made at Marye's Hill, and there the Irish Brigade gave an exhibit of courage which in the record of American valor may have been matched but was never surpassed.

As the heads of the attacking column came within range, Longstreet's guns spoke, the earth shook, and clouds of bitter, blue-gray smoke, streaked with lightning flashes, enveloped the long crest of Marye's Hill. Below on the plain solid shot, grape, and canister tore through the blue lines. Shells exploded overhead. While drums thrashed and bugles screamed, the men closed up broken ranks and maintained their steady step.

When they neared the stone wall, muskets, rifles, and heads suddenly appeared above it and a storm of lead smote the marchers. Flag-bearers faltered and banners fell, but amid cheers fresh hands lifted the colors and the charge rolled on. Then a gray death cloud arose and wound itself about the hand-to-hand struggle. When it drifted away it revealed scattered blue fragments creeping back from the gallant but hopeless charge. Confederate guns sought out the thinned ranks and showered them with iron.

Five times Meagher led the attacking wave against the stone wall and five times it recoiled.

To reach the enemy, after the first attack, the returning men stepped over their own wounded, dying, and dead. Each time there were less in the reforming ranks, more lying on the battlefield. General Longstreet himself said that the wounded fell like the steady dropping of rain from the eaves of a house.

Lee watched the hopeless Union attacks, and spoke with admiration of Meagher and the Brigade. "Never were men so brave," he asserted. "They ennobled their race by their splendid gallantry on that desperate occasion. Though totally routed, they reaped harvests of glory. Their brilliant though hopeless assaults on our lines excited the hearty applause of our officers and soldiers."

After the sixth unsuccessful assault, darkness mercifully ended the fighting for the day.

All commands in the attack on Marye's Hill had suffered terrible casualties. Hancock took 5006 men of his division into the fight, and lost 2013, of whom 156 were commissioned officers. The percentage of loss of the Irish Brigade was comparable to that of the whole division. Meagher rode toward Marye's Hill with 1415 men marching behind him. When the last attack was over, only 874 remained. Killed and wounded he had lost 541, of whom 53 were commissioned officers. Some of his regiments lost half their men.

The portion of the plain between the canal and the stone wall over which the Union forces made their attack had an area of about ten or twelve acres. Within that space on the night of December 13, the dead and wounded averaged a thousand to an acre. And one out of every twenty casualties was a member of the small Irish Brigade. The stretcher-bearers and burial squads recognized the Irish by the sprigs of green in their caps.

Chapter IX

A BLIZZARD OF FIRE

NEWS waited for Meagher as he followed his commands back into Fredericksburg after the failure of the last attack on Marye's Hill. The long-expected battle flags had finally arrived from New York.

Wounded, dying, and dead filled the streets of the town and "stretched in a hideous carpet along the stone fence at the foot of the Hill." That night the remnants of the Brigade bivouacked in Fredericksburg.

Many soldiers were extremely angry, some of the generals to the point of insubordination. They had seen thousands of the best soldiers in the Union army slaughtered in hopeless attacks. Meagher's temper boiled.

To house the flag-presentation ceremonies, the Irish Brigade had constructed a large hall in its camp north of the river.

"Will we wait until we recross the Rappahannock to present the flags to our regiments?" someone asked.

Meagher's eyes flashed and his mouth grew grim. "We will present them here, unless we cross before tomorrow night."

"But our hall is across the river."

"Then we will use the Fredericksburg theater."

And so, while burial parties gathered the dead and the wounded were carried in long processions over the pontoon bridges, aides rode out with invitations to a selected list of officers of the army.

Anxious for a victory whatever the cost, Burnside would have renewed the hopeless attacks the next morning, but the good sense of some of his better officers prevailed. That day the hurt Union army quietly licked its wounds.

Toward evening on December 15, notables crowded into the small Fredericksburg theater. Meagher presided as toastmaster. Around the speakers' table, which was set on the stage, twenty-two generals gathered. Seats had been removed from the main floor. Officers of the Brigade and their guests lined the walls. In the center of the floor two rows of tables held food and drink. The delicacies had been cooked in neighboring houses and were served by a corps of military waiters.

The booming of Confederate artillery on Marye's Hill and the screaming and bursting of shells provided a fitting if somewhat terrifying background for the ceremonies. Soon it became apparent that the theater itself was the target. A sharp-sighted Confederate artilleryman had seen an unusual number of high Union officers gather there. He guessed that an important meeting was being held. And so the shelling began.

After dinner, Meagher rose to present the flags to the commander of each of his regiments. The American and Irish banners of beautifully embroidered silk lay before him. The four colonels stepped forward, and with appropriate remarks Meagher made the presentations. Each colonel accepted his flags, and then returned them.

Meagher later explained to the donors: "Many a brave officer — many a brave soldier — who had looked forward to their arrival lay dead in his frozen blood that evening on the battlefield, denied forever the satisfaction he had glowingly cherished in anticipation. Their comrades received the colors with pride, with gratefulness, with the loftiest enthusiasm — " and then "declined to receive and carry them, stating that their numbers had been so reduced, that they could not in conscience undertake to defend with honor, treasures that were, and ever should be, infinitely dearer to them than their lives."

Some of the guests at first had questioned the sense and taste of holding a public banquet in the midst of a defeated army and a ruined town, while burial squads gathered the dead. Gradually they understood Meagher's purpose. He was indignant at the incompetence that had killed brave men to no advantage.

Meagher raised his glass to toast this close friend, General Alfred Sully. "I have the honor to ask you to drink to the health of my esteemed friend; and I want you to understand that *he* is not one of your 'Political Generals,' but a brave and accomplished soldier — who attracted his 'star' from the firmament of glory — by the electricity of his sword."

Meagher's meaning was unmistakable. The Union armies had been cursed by the appointment of incompetent politicians to high commands, and by battles into which generals were pushed for political rather than military reasons. Meagher was thinking of the brave soldiers dead or maimed, who from Bull Run to Fredericksburg had been uselessly, needlessly slaughtered.

The speech Meagher made that evening was never published. It is not likely he wrote it in advance. Certainly on the day following a terrible defeat, while the stricken army lay under the enemy's guns, and more than a third of his command had been killed or wounded, he had more important matters to attend to than writing a speech. After he finished with it, those who heard it whispered that Meagher's chief reason for insisting that the ceremony should be held immediately was to protest against poor leadership in Washington and in the field. The bitter truths which he stated gave mortal offense to the people he described. The officers of the army of the Potomac called the ceremony "Meagher's Death Feast."

During the speeches the bombardment of the theater went on. At first the guests paid little attention to the noise. The aim of the Confederate gunners seemed bad. Shells and solid shot whistled high overhead and exploded or landed harmlessly far beyond the building.

Gradually the sounds came nearer. Now the missiles skimmed the roof of the theater, the shells exploding nearby with a violence that shook the dishes on the table. Clearly the Confederate gunners were finding the range. The gold-braided audience in the theater began to move uncomfortably. With one ear they listened to the speaker; with the other, to the boom of the cannon and the howl and explosion of the shells.

The climax came when a solid shot knocked down a small stone house within a few yards of the theater. The thump jolted everybody. The speaker looked astonished, and for a moment was silent. Although the audience looked toward the exits, the program went on.

It ended a few tense minutes afterward when a waiter — one of Meagher's orderlies — entered the theater holding his tray high. The guests stared. He had picked up the cannon ball in the wreckage of the collapsed house. He carried it on his tray. Openmouthed, the speaker stopped in the middle of a sentence, and the generals, colonels, and other officers poured from the building and mounted their horses, each man finding as best he could his way through the night to his own command. During the night and the next morning the army recrossed the Rappahannock.

Among those killed at Fredericksburg was Meagher's close friend, William Horgan of the 88th, who had enlisted as a private and risen to be a major. Meagher instructed the burial squads to make a special effort to find Horgan. He had the body embalmed and, as soon as his lameness permitted, accompanied it back to New York, arriving at noon on Christmas day.

His lameness, however, proved serious and he went to bed. He arose to attend Horgan's funeral and then returned to bed for another two weeks. While he was convalescing, the officers of the Irish Brigade presented him with a gold medal in "Testimony of His Gallant and Patriotic Services in the Cause of the American Union, and His Devotion to the Brigade."

When Meagher returned to Virginia, the Irish Brigade lay in winter quarters near Falmouth, which is north of the Rappahannock and near Fredericksburg. Apparently the War Department — and that meant Secretary Edwin M. Stanton, who ruled the department as a tyrant — was angry with Meagher because he had been among the first to speak out against the incompetence in high places, which had resulted in the aimless slaughter at Fredericksburg.

When the Irish Brigade lined up for review, Meagher frowned.

During the four months of inactivity between the battles of Antietam and Fredericksburg, many New England regiments had been permitted to return home and "recruit." This was a much-sought-after privilege, since it not only gave a command a chance to rebuild to its proper strength, but provided the men with an opportunity to rest and to see their families and friends. Some regiments so favored had more men in their ranks than were left altogether in the four regiments of the Irish Brigade.

In private Meagher spoke bitterly to his fellow officers: "Before Fredericksburg, President Lincoln, Secretary Stanton, and General Halleck admitted the justice of my claim that while the army lay in winter quarters the Irish Brigade should be permitted to recruit. Yet they did nothing about it."

"But they allowed many New England regiments to recruit, General."

"Yes. And at Fredericksburg we lost a third of the few men we had left. What do the muster rolls of the three New York regiments show as present and fit for duty?"

"Only 521 men."

"Why the 69th alone once could muster 1300 men. They won't let us recruit, and they expect the 521 of us to carry out the assignments of three regiments of a thousand men each. In other words they expect us to occupy a brigade front in the line, and each man to carry out the duties of six."

It was clear that the Irish Brigade was not being dealt with fairly. The reason is not hard to guess: Meagher's "death feast" must have been reported to Burnside. And Burnside must have referred the matter to Lincoln and Stanton. Burnside had similar complaints to make about other officers, some of them major generals in top places. He even asked Lincoln to court-martial General Hooker on the charge of insubordination.

It is likely, too, that the War Department read the comment made by an officer of the Irish Brigade who was in New York, recovering from wounds when Fredericksburg was fought: "May God visit a just judgment on the man or men who caused so much good, true, loyal blood to be shed in vain; so many brave children of the people to be led up to slaughter, destruction, to the coldest-blooded murder. For of a surety it was all this — it was destruction, slaughter, murder."

"I still hope for fair treatment from the War Department," Meagher said, as he sat down on February 20, 1863, to write a lengthy appeal to Secretary Stanton.

In this document he set forth the services of the Brigade, its losses, duties, and its inability to recruit while remaining in the field. Because the three New York regiments had given the longest service in the Brigade and had suffered the greatest losses, he made a special plea for them. They at least should be given a chance to return home and build up their man power. In making this request, he pointed out, he was asking for no special or unusual privileges. He sought only that which had been "conceded to other commands."

No reply came. The request was not granted. The letter was not even acknowledged.

And so one man of the Irish Brigade continued to try to do the work of six. Meanwhile, Burnside had been replaced as commander of the army of the Potomac by General Joseph Hooker.

The great day of the year for an Irishman is St. Patrick's Day, March 17. With the first signs of spring in Maryland, the thoughts of the Irish turned to the feast of their beloved patron. Picket duty, drill, mess routines, policing had worn their spirits thin. To break the monotony with some fun, Meagher set the Brigade to making preparations for a monster St. Patrick's Day celebration.

"What are you Irishmen building over there?" the Germans in the 11th Corps asked.

"Sure, and its a chapel we're putting up, so that we can invite you to Mass when the good Father celebrates the feast of the blessed St. Patrick."

The chapel was a giant framework of boards and poles, covered with the canvas of many tents. When it was finished, the loyal sons of St. Patrick decorated it inside and out with wreaths, festoons, and bouquets. All were carefully bunched or braided of evergreens.

In front of General Hancock's headquarters the men erected three spacious stands. These overlooked an open field where races and games were to be held. One stand was reserved for generals, another for the judges of the race course, and a third for ladies. High officers frequently brought their wives to camp for long visits.

Meagher's aides carried written invitations to important personages, and the whole Brigade invited the rest of the army by word of mouth. From late afternoon until midnight on the eve of the feast, the Irish fife and drum corps paraded along the Union line, squealing and rattling at one tune — probably "All Praise to St. Patrick." No one could be unmindful of the significance of the morrow for the Irish. Father Corby, the chaplain, heard hundreds of confessions that day.

Next morning all roads led to Falmouth, and every soldier who could get away walked or rode toward Hancock's division. Hooker and his staff arrived early. Hooker rode his familiar white horse and was greeted with cheers. Prominent visitors were shown the best seats in the canvas chapel. The rest crowded in and overflowed onto the parade ground.

When Father Corby began High Mass, the men of the Brigade beamed and nudged one another. "The vestments — " they whispered.

Father was elegant in new vestments. The men had taken up a collection to buy them for him. Two soldiers served as acolytes, and the Mass was accompanied by martial music. At its close, Father O'Hagan, chaplain of the "Excelsior Brigade," preached a sermon described as "eloquent and patriotic." Meagher looked around him during the ceremony. He had invited hundreds of army guests, and they had come.

The crowd was colorful. The army of the Potomac was famous for its variety of uniforms, and Zouaves in red or white breeches, embroidered jackets of many colors, and tasseled caps, mingled with men in regulation blue. Artillerymen gossiped with infantry. Mounted or afoot, men pushed their way through the crowd. English, French, German, and Gaelic were bantered, with snatches of Hungarian or Russian. Gold braid and buttons and dress swords added glint and glitter to the gathering, and thousands of shoulder straps showed that the commissioned officers were well represented from lieutenant to major general.

Most conspicuous of all by his bearing, dress, and function as host and master of ceremonies, was Meagher himself.

He was dressed elegantly for the occasion, wearing a tall white hat, a rich, full green necktie, a brown coat with a rosette of blue ribbon on it (blue is the old color of Ireland), white gloves, and white silk-velvet half breeches. He rode astride a prancing reddish-gray horse and carried in his hand a long-lashed whip. He seemed to be everywhere, welcoming guests, keeping the program moving. His voice rang out above all noise and confusion. His assistant master of ceremonies was General Caldwell, who commanded another brigade in Hancock's division of Sumner's Corps.

After Mass, Hooker took his place in the reviewing stand. A distinguished group of generals surrounded him. Someone handed Hooker a glass of wine.

"The Irish Brigade — God bless them!"

He held up his hand and in the hush continued: "I want three cheers for the Irish Brigade. Hip-hip-hurray! Hip-hip-hurray! Hip-hip-hurray!" The roar of cheers must have reached the Confederate lines south of the river.

Races and games filled the forenoon. At noon, Meagher invited his guests to Brigade headquarters. Here mounds of sandwiches and a punch bowl — half a whisky keg festooned with evergreen — waited for them. For entertainment, the poet of the Brigade delivered a poetical address of welcome in which he praised McClellan and Hooker, but criticized those responsible for the disaster at Fredricksburg.

As the last foot race of the afternoon was run, heavy firing on the right of the Union army began.

"The Confederates are going to attack," the generals agreed.

"It would be in keeping with what's happened before," Meagher joked. "In the Irish Brigade, most 'big days' end in a fight.

"Join your commands immediately, gentlemen," Hooker ordered, and as his officers rode off, and he prepared to mount, he expressed the thought that everyone had in mind: "It's too bad that St. Patrick's Day comes only once a year."

In ten minutes the stands and sidelines were emptied, and only the Irish Brigade remained on the drill field. After a few minutes of cannonading, the Confederate guns grew silent. No attack was made that day. Perhaps the Irish in the Confederate army were making their own contribution of noise in honor of their patron saint.

For another month the army under Hooker remained in its winter quarters in comparative quiet, readying itself for the summer campaign. By the end of April the return of the wounded and the arrival of new recruits swelled its ranks to over 100,000. The army of Lee, which it faced, lay 60,000 strong south of the Rappahannock, behind a line of entrenched positions extending for twenty-five miles.

As spring came on, with the army growing impatient, Meagher was called back to New York to assist in the cause of suffering Ireland. The potato crop had failed again and famine blighted the land. A meeting was called at the Academy of Music to raise funds. The mayor of New York presided, and among the speakers were Archbishop Hughes, General McClellan, Horace Greeley, America's most famous editor, and General Meagher.

Meagher talked about Ireland, "bowed down though she be, steeped in gall, gnawed with misery to the bone." The poor, the ragged, the famishing of Ireland should have taken heart from the Irish soldier fighting for his adopted country. He never lost sight of the mountains on which his eyes first opened. He could not forget Ireland.

On his return to the army on April 26, 1863, Meagher was told to report to Hancock for orders before rejoining the Irish Brigade, which waited at one of the fords to cross the Rappahannock. By the time Meagher reached the Brigade, the whole army was in motion.

In spite of the fact that his ranks were not yet filled, by early April Hooker became impatient. The term of enlistment of many of his troops would soon expire. The weather was right for campaigning. Hooker made several attempts to compel Lee to retreat from his Fredericksburg position.

First he sent a strong force of cavalry to destroy the railroads in Lee's rear. When this expedition failed Hooker tried to turn Lee's flank. To do this he sent 10,000 cavalry to raid Lee from the rear. Next he ordered the left wing of the Union army to feint an attack on the Confederate right. While Lee was concerned about driving back the Union left, Hooker sent

36,000 men of his right wing to cross the Rappahannock and march quietly around Lee's left to Chancellorsville. There, between Lee's army and Richmond, they were to halt and entrench.

The men from Hooker's right reached Chancellorsville on the evening of April 30, and bivouacked in the wilderness, a region of woods and heavy thicket.

In Hooker's advance to Chancellorsville, the Irish Brigade formed the extreme right of the Second Army Corps. On the night of April 30, the Brigade crossed the Rappahannock in the moonlight and bivouacked on the southern bank, guarding a ford near the main road from Richmond to Chancellorsville.

All the next day it marched, and at 10 that night reached Scott's Mills, a position which it was ordered to defend.

Meagher looked at his map by lantern light.

"Here we are at Scott's Mills. There is Chancellorsville a couple of miles from us. And this road connects directly with the Confederate left."

He turned to the Brigade officers. "You can see why our army must hold this point. Post pickets, make loopholes for sharpshooters in the walls of the Mill and the outbuilding. Captain, see that our six guns are so placed as to cover our position."

Throughout the night and during the next day the Brigade guarded the ford. Meanwhile at 8 in the morning heavy fire from the direction of Chancellorsville told that a desperate battle was being fought. Instead of fleeing toward Richmond as Hooker expected, Lee turned and fought. Lee was abler than Hooker, and he saw that Hooker had made a serious mistake in dividing his vastly superior army. As long as Lee could fight one part of Hooker's army at a time, the odds were much more even.

And so he struck at that part of the Union army which Hooker had led to Chancellorsville. He wanted to keep the Union army divided and thus compel Hooker to fight at a disadvantage.

To make the attack, Lee sent Stonewall Jackson, on the morning of May 1, to attack the Union troops at Chancellorsville. Jackson succeeded in pushing the Union army back into their entrenchments, but failed to carry these.

Although both armies were now in difficult positions, Hooker decided to remain on the defensive, while Lee made up his mind to attack again. Lee's plan was brilliant, and would have been exceedingly risky had not the brilliant Jackson been his right-hand man. Lee decided to surprise Hooker by dividing the Confederate army and sending Jackson with 25,000 men to march rapidly and fall on Hooker's rear. This movement was screened by the wilderness. The surprise worked. Terrible panic resulted in the Union army.

Meagher learned what happened, when suddenly the road and the woods in his front became alive with fugitives in blue.

"We were surprised," big-eyed men cried breathlessly.

"Stonewall Jackson is coming with the whole of Lee's army."

"We told them that we were being outflanked, and no one paid attention to us."

Out of the confusion the Irish Brigade pieced together the story. The fugitives belonged to the Eleventh Corps. The officers had not heeded the warnings of the men that they were being surrounded and would not look or listen or believe the clear signs that the Confederates were marching through the woods.

Then suddenly Jackson's yelling divisions burst upon them. After sustaining heavy losses, the Eleventh Corps broke and fled panic-stricken.

Their flight brought them to Scott's Mills. To halt the fugitives, Meagher threw a line of soldiers with bayonets fixed across the road and into the woods. Thus he prevented the panic of the Eleventh Corps from turning into the rout of Hooker's army.

In the great fight that day, all the troops, North and South, near Chancellorsville, participated. That evening in the dusk, Jackson was mistaken for a Union cavalryman and mortally wounded by his own soldiers.

When Hooker tried to bring more of his army to Chancellorsville, Lee drove back the reinforcements.

At 8 o'clock the next morning, Sunday, May 3, Meagher received orders to enter the battle. He was to lead the Brigade to the front, and there support the Fifth Maine Battery, which stood at the opening of the woods commanding the plain at Chancellorsville.

After two hours of difficult marching, much of it under heavy fire, the Brigade reached its assigned position. Meagher rode at the head of his men through a shower of shot, shell, and falling branches. Several times he narrowly escaped death. One shell burst directly behind him, killing one man and wounding three others.

A cheer of welcome from the few survivors of the hard-pressed battery greeted the rescuing column. All the battery horses had been killed, all the men killed or wounded, and the battery was being destroyed by a wounded corporal and a wounded soldier. When Meagher appeared, these two had just blown up the caissons, and the Confederates were advancing to seize the guns.

The Irish Brigade poured into the gap in the line and with one volley checked the enemy. Meanwhile, under orders from Meagher, a detachment laid hold of the ropes and dragged the guns to safety in the woods. As the Brigade reached the plain with the rescued guns General Hancock rode up.

"General Meagher," Hancock shouted above the noise of the battle, "you command the retreat."

Hooker's army was still divided, while Lee's was reunited. To save himself Hooker was evacuating his strong positions on the roads to the rear of Chancellorsville.

That Sunday evening the Irish Brigade occupied the woods to the left of one of the battlefield landmarks, the "White House." There throughout the night and into the morning the men used shovels instead of guns and constructed a strong line of breastworks.

During Monday, although enemy batteries shelled the woods and killed and wounded some of the Brigade, the Confederates did not attack it. Again Meagher had a close escape when a cannon ball struck a tree near which he stood.

When on Wednesday, May 6, the Union army recrossed the Rappahannock to occupy its old camps on the Fredericksburg heights, the Irish Brigade marched back with fifty men less than it had before Chancellorsville. While this loss could not compare with the terrible casualties which it suffered at Antietam and Fredericksburg, it now was only a skeleton of what it had been.

Almost three months had now passed since Meagher wrote to the War Department asking the same treatment for the Brigade that other brigades received. The letter was still unacknowledged, the request not granted.

And so in protest, on May 8, 1863, Meagher resigned his command, pointing out to General Hancock that he wished to cease being commander of "what was once known as the Irish Brigade. That Brigade no longer exists. A mere handful," the Brigade did its duty at Chancellorsville. "But I cannot be party to the wrong. My heart, my conscience, my pride, all that is truthful, sincere and just within me, forbid it." Nevertheless, in tendering this resignation Meagher wanted the War Department to understand that his "services, in any capacity that can prove useful, are freely at the summons and disposition of the government of the United States." The unfriendly War Department lost no time in accepting the resignation.

In the evening of the day on which the acceptance came, the Brigade formed into a hollow square, with Meagher and his staff and friends in the middle, to say good-by to their much-loved commander. The band played, Meagher spoke, and the men gave nine enthusiastic cheers for him. Then the commissioned officers, one by one, stepped forward and shook his hand. Finally, Meagher went around the square and shook the hand of each man, saying, "Good-by. And God bless you."

With that, the tearful-eyed men returned to their quarters and, deeply touched, the officers for the last time joined in a social evening with the commander who had shared the fortunes of war with them from Bull Run to Chancellorsville.

The quiet talk at headquarters spanned three continents and many storms. The next morning Meagher was gone.

The "Fighting Irish" became a legend in the American army, and their reputation for gallantry, won under Meagher in the battlefields of the Civil War, was kept alive by a great regiment from New York in other wars, sons, grandsons, and great-grandsons of Meagher's men.

Chapter X

STORMS' END

For Meagher there was no more marching through the night to misty morning battlefields, no clear call of brassy trumpets sounding charge, no frenzied scramble to cross trenches blazing with fire and leaden rain and iron hail.

By the end of May, 1863, he reached New York and was paid high honors by the city of his adoption.

If the War Department slighted him, Lincoln dealt with him more justly. Several times during the war it seemed that the unfriendliness of certain members of the English government toward the Union would put England fighting on the side of the Confederacy. In these crises Lincoln appeared unwilling to compromise the national honor.

"It seems to me," Meagher told his friends, "that if we find ourselves fighting the English and Confederates at the same time, it might be practical to recruit American soldiers of Irish birth for service in Ireland."

Undoubtedly he dreamed of leading an American brigade in Ireland, as he led an Irish brigade in America. In any event, in June, 1863, he offered to raise 3000 Irish troops, probably for that purpose.

Although Lincoln accepted the offer, before Meagher could begin to recruit guns boomed out all over the North on the Fourth of July, 1863, to tell the war-weary nation that each of the three biggest Union armies had scored a great victory. In the east the army of the Potomac, under Meade, who had succeeded Hooker in command, had turned back Lee at Gettysburg. In the middle territory, the army of the Cumberland, under Rosecrans, in the greatest bloodless victory of the war, had pushed Bragg and the Confederate line back of the Tennessee River. And in the west, the army of the Mississippi, under Grant, had captured Vicksburg. With Union armies victorious, and the Union navy blockading the South and controlling the seas, the chances of foreign interference were greatly lessened, and Meagher's scheme came to naught.

By the fall of 1864 the occupation of much of the South by Northern armies made necessary the setting up of military governments. The occupied territories were divided into districts governed by generals and policed by garrisons of soldiers.

In recognition of his services, Lincoln appointed Meagher to serve in the Provisional Division of the Army of the Tennessee. He was ordered to report to Major General James B. Stedman at Chattanooga. Stedman was in charge of the military district of Etowah.

When Stedman was ordered to report to General George H. Thomas at Nashville, Meagher took temporary command of the district, with jurisdiction over 12,000 infantry, two regiments of cavalry, several batteries of field artillery, and the strong fortifications of Chattanooga. These mounted many heavy guns. This was the largest, though not the most important, command held by Meagher during the war.

Atlanta had fallen to Sherman. Lee was making a last desperate stand on the Petersburg-Richmond Line. Thomas had scattered Hood's army at Nashville. The Confederacy was too weak to live; too strong to die without a lingering, hopeless struggle. Now Sherman must march to the sea, cut the South in half, bring the war to a civilian population far behind the fighting front, destroy the granary out of which the Southern armies ate, and cut the railroads that tied the South together.

Meagher had seen evictions in Ireland. He understood full well the suffering of helpless women and children, the sick, the poor, the aged. He had no taste for burning and looting. One of his first and most vivid impressions of the war was the needless burning of a house on the Bull Run battlefield. He called the hand that set the fire "scurvy and malignant," and the men responsible for it "ruffians." He pointed out that the Irish Brigade went out "to fight and put down the armed enemies of the Republic, and not to cast naked and breadless on the world, the women, children, and aged fathers of the delinquent states," and to destroy their houses, cattle, gardens, cornfields, and other property.

The plan had been to detach a strong body of veterans from the 15th and 17th Corps, give the command to Meagher, and send him with Sherman on the March to the Sea.

Meagher had asked to be returned to active service. But he wanted to lead soldiers against soldiers, and not against women, children, and old folks. Rather than violate his principles, he declined the opportunity.

Shortly after the beginning of 1865 he resigned from the army. Less than two months later Lee surrendered at Appomattox, and in a few days the war was over.

In July, 1865, President Andrew Johnson, who succeeded Lincoln, appointed Meagher as Secretary of the Territory of Montana. For three years Meagher gave excellent service in the post. He loved the wild beauties of the frontier territory.

Toward the beginning of July, 1868, while serving as acting governor as well as secretary, he rode thirty miles on horseback under a hot sun to Benton on the Missouri River, to await a shipment of arms from the government. Although he had not been well for about three weeks, and was ill when he arrived, he spent the afternoon conversing and writing on business matters. Trying to find a comfortable place to sleep, he occupied the pilot's quarters on the river steamboat *G. A. Thompson,* which was moored to the dock. The Missouri was flooding and turbulent.

During the night, Meagher grew distressingly restless, and leaving the cabin, he accidently wandered near the steamboat's rail. The guard for the rail was broken and Meagher fell into the river.

The deck sentry saw a moving shadow in the starless night and heard a noise from the stern deck. Then a shout for help pierced the darkness and the sentry cried, "Man overboard!" An Indian raid had caused the crew to prepare for emergencies. Now in a moment the deck was alive, lanterns were lighted, life bouys were cast on the waters, and small boats were launched. But Meagher had been swept away and drowned in the broiling waters. His body was never recovered.

Slowly the news reached the East. When New York learned of it, the Irish Brigade marched to a Requiem High Mass in the Church of St. Francis Xavier. Father Lory, the Brigade chaplain, was the celebrant. In remembrance of Fredericksburg, the officers wore a sprig of evergreen in their hats. The 69th attended in uniform.

That evening, at the Cooper Institute, the Honorable Richard O'Gorman pronounced Meagher's eulogy. A thousand of the eloquent sentences could be quoted. One must suffice: "In Ireland, in America, he invited no man to any danger that he was not ready to share. May he rest in peace."

❁ ❁ ❁

The story is often repeated how in 1871, when a

Sir Charles Duffy was elected prime minister of the Australian state of Victoria, Queen Victoria was astonished to learn that this was the same Charles Duffy, the Young Ireland rebel, whom, twenty-three years before, her court had sentenced to be hanged, drawn, and quartered for treason. The Queen had commuted the sentence to transportation.

Her curiosity was aroused, and she asked, "What happened to the eight others who were transported at the same time?"

The records were brought out.

Morris Lyene had been attorney general of Australia.

Michael Ireland succeeded him as attorney general of Australia.

Richard O'Gorman was the governor-general of Newfoundland.

Thomas McGee was president of the Council for the Dominion of Canada.

John Mitchel was a prominent New York politician.

Patrick Donahue had been a brigadier general in the United States army.

Terence McManus had been a brigadier general in the United States army.

Thomas Francis Meagher had been a brigadier general in the United States army; commander of the Irish Brigade; distinguished editor, writer, and journalist; one of the greatest of orators, Irish and American; and secretary and acting governor of Montana.

A great American writer, Claude G. Bowers, historian, diplomat, and orator, has written of Meagher that it may "truly be said that his entire life was dedicated to the cause of liberty. Wherever he was placed he found work to do, and he possessed the genius to meet it. His speech on the sword alone entitles him to a high place among the orators of his century. His relation to the rising of 1848 would alone make him a treasured memory wherever freedom has a worshiper. His superb gallantry at Fredericksburg alone would assure him a place in history among the bravest of the brave.

"Orator, protagonist, soldier, dreamer, and doer, Thomas Francis Meagher will live in the affection of his race as long as the green hills of old Ireland loom above the wave."

The writer of this simple life of Thomas Francis Meagher acknowledges his indebtedness at every turn to a book with a long title: *Memoirs of Gen. Thomas Francis Meagher, Comprising the Leading Events of His Career, Chronologically Arranged with Selections from His Speeches, Lectures and Miscellaneous Writings, Including Personal Reminiscences.* This book of 498 pages of text and an appendix of 38 pages was written by Michael Cavanaugh, secretary to John O'Mahoney, H.C., Fenian Brotherhood. It was published by the Messenger Press, Worcester, Massachusetts, in 1892.

The brief notices on Irish history were checked against a simple text: A. M. Nolan's *A History of Ireland,* J. S. Hyland and Company, publishers, Chicago, Illinois, 345 pages.

A reference was made to *The Irish Orators,* by Claude G. Bowers. This book of 525 pages, published by Bobbs-Merrill Company, Inc., Indianapolis, Indiana, copyright 1916, 1944, discusses the nine greatest orators in a nation famed for oratory. Thomas Francis Meagher is one of these. He is treated on pages 328–372. The quotation is used by special permission of the publishers.